A Gallery of
WOMEN

THEODORE
DREISER

In Two Volumes
—

VOLUME II

NEW YORK
HORACE LIVERIGHT
1929

Contents

OF VOLUME TWO

REGINA C——   429

RELLA   479

ERNESTINE   527

RONA MURTHA   565

IDA HAUCHAWOUT   625

EMANUELA   661

ESTHER NORN   723

BRIDGET MULLANPHY   777

REGINA C——

Regina C——

In the face of all the morality that is preached in the world I have been more than once sharply arrested mentally by those who are not moral, who are not even interested by such moral or balanced conduct as guides some others, religiously and ethically, who from the beginning give themselves over to conduct which flouts most of our accepted rules. And who fare how? What is their end? Is it true that unless one does thus and so, conducts himself according to the standard of give and take which prevails in the simpler walks of life, one does not fare so well as those who do so conform?

Regina C——, the figure of this sketch, never so conformed, in so far as I could gather. She remained indeed independent of all those binding emotions and tendernesses which hold most families and friends together. She was, according to one of her friends, the victim of an incurable passion, not so much for a man, (who chanced, however, to be the nucleus of the same), as for a place. Read and consider. She was, and remains, a riddle to me. She may, and she may not, prove to be one to you.

The first time I saw her was at a party which by some might be considered loose, but was really nothing more than a genial "gab-fest" given one evening in the rooms of a young woman successful as a motion picture star. One small group was playing cards; another sat about a table and drank, or, tiring of that, adjourned to a larger room to dance to the music of the victrola or player-piano. There was much banter, jesting, laughter, all the silly arguments, slurs and quips that come under the heading of a good time.

But in the midst of it, about eleven-thirty or twelve o'clock, there swept into the room, with a refreshing dash, a girl who at once interested me. She was tall and dark, with a waxy-tan complexion, large, interesting, and, I should say, confused eyes. Long, loose capes were then the mode, and she was wearing one, together with a hat that somehow suited the contour of her face and coloring. Any one would have said on sight I think that she was modish, sophisticated, and probably clever. With an offhand air of familiarity, she threw off her cape and hat, brushed back her hair with one sweep of her hand, and exclaimed: "Whoopee! I'm glad to be over here again, you bet!"

"Why the sudden haste, old top?" called one girl, banteringly.

"You certainly blow in like a March wind, Regina. They don't close doors down where you come from, do they?" (She had left the hall door open.)

"Oh, shut up," was her response. "Give me a drink, will you? Gee, I wish you all knew how I got here.

Didn't even have a notion of coming until four-thirty; then I threw some things into a bag and caught the five-thirty. But the way I did it! Didn't even pay my fare."

She went to the table and picked up a glass and filled it, dashed into another room with it to greet those who were playing cards, then returned to the center room, where, seeing a man she knew, she suggested that they dance. Forthwith, they joined several others who were pirouetting about the room.

I asked a girl who sat near me about her, and was told that she was formerly a trained nurse but now a superintendent of nurses in a private hospital in Washington. She knew little more than that about her. But as the evening wore on, and after all but a few who knew the newcomer very well had departed, Regina launched into a brisk account of how, having made up her mind to come to New York, and lacking the necessary cash at the moment, she had gone to the station in Washington with the deliberate intention of interesting some man—any man, apparently, only she did not put it quite so baldly—to pay her fare. Having found such a person, who no doubt fancied that she was entering upon an affair with him, she chatted amiably enough with him until they reached the station in New York, where she excused herself to visit the ladies' room. There she waited until she saw him gazing interestedly at a window display in the station, and then slipped out, bag in hand, coming straight to this place. "I hope I never run into him again," was her closing comment.

For a girl holding a responsible position, even though young and attractive, this struck me as a cool proceeding. For why such a gay, inconsequential superintendent of nurses? Was it by such that our hospitals were being run? Heaven guard the poor patients. I was puzzled, and a few days later asked a Miss Redmond whom I knew, and who had been pointed out as one of her friends, about her.

"Oh, Regina," she said, indifferently. "It's a long story. My sister and I knew her in Washington. She seems a little crazy sometimes, but she's far from that. She's as shrewd and clever as can be. You wouldn't think she was a graduate chemist and bacteriologist, would you?"

"Well, not exactly. No."

"But she is. And up to last week she was superintendent of a small hospital in Washington. She's in love with a surgeon here, but they've quarreled and I suppose she's over here to make it up."

"Yes . . . but how about her fare? Couldn't she pay that?"

"She could. Only that's her way. She preferred to make somebody else pay it—to play a trick on some one. That's Regina for you. She's the coldest and meanest of girls in some ways."

"And yet she appears to have charm."

"Lots of it. Only she doesn't really care for anybody. But I can't tell you now. It's too long a story."

And there the matter rested.

But for the life of me I could not get out of my mind the incident in the apartment, her appearance and that peculiarly cold, bald story, told with so much effrontery before others. They were all good friends, to be sure, but why such an open, indifferent, non-self-protective picture of herself and her ways?

Chancing a few weeks later to be visiting Miss Redmond, the doorbell rang and in walked, or rather rushed, this same Regina, dressed this time in sport clothes and looking very gay and spring-like. She and a certain Wally, the surgeon above mentioned, as she breathlessly explained, were out for a drive to some inn up the Hudson shore. Wouldn't we come along? It was so fine out, just the night for a drive. Come on! Again I noted the vigor and dash, an almost irritating energy which seemed not to let her rest for a moment. Even as she talked she was here and there about the room, commenting on this, that, and other episodes with which both she and Miss Redmond seemed familiar. Only Miss Redmond was not in the mood for driving. Another night, possibly. Regina dashed out, and that was the end of that. Curious as to this latest development, and with the thought of the stranger who had been left at the station still fresh in my mind, I asked: "And is Wally the surgeon she came back to see?"

"Uh-huh. He's having her reappointed superintendent of a hospital here. She was here once before, but left. They're always quarreling, or she is. She treats him like a dog. I don't know why he stands it. But she's coming back now, or so she says, because they can't get along without her."

"Well, I can see how a surgeon might be interested in such a vigorous dynamic girl."

"She is vigorous and dynamic, all right. She's a regular wild cat sometimes. But I don't like her so very much. She's too cold and hard. She only likes to play when she wants to. And she hasn't any sense of responsibility or honor. But that's her affair, and his." She relapsed into silence.

I was really interested by this strange girl, and by degrees wormed out of Marie the following bit of autobiography:

"I was living with my sister in Washington when I met Regina. You've seen how attractive she is. She was always well-dressed and carried herself with an inimitable air that must have been born in her. It could never have been acquired. Her education had never gone farther than a high school, but she used exquisite English always. She claimed to be from a very good Virginia family, and we always ragged her about being an F.F.V. Her father, according to hints from her, had been wild and treated her mother so badly that she had died of the conventional Southern broken heart when Regina was only a year or so old. The home was broken up and the children, two boys and two girls, put out among various relatives. Regina had no least family feeling, which I laid to her having been separated from her family for so long. Her sister was living in Washington with an aunt, but Regina paid no attention to her. She called her conventional and dull, while she herself liked to dance until morning and sneak up or down hospital fire-escapes at six A.M. I don't know where the brothers were, and I doubt if she knew. The father was living in Newark, but he and Regina never exchanged visits or letters. She was entirely alone, and as soon as she finished her hospital training she rented a one-room and bath apartment and furnished it daintily with wicker furniture, intending to go on nursing cases in order to make her living. Like most Southerners, she loved work so well she could lie down and go to sleep beside it and never be troubled in the least. She never took a case as long as she had a dollar in her pocket.

"I met her when she had just taken her apartment and was stepping out into life. During her training she had fallen in love with a young surgeon connected with the hospital, but I don't think he cared very much for her. He was your typical ambitious medico, young and alive and determined not to be satisfied to follow in the path which the older men of his profession had blazed. Already he was doing big things, so he thought, in surgery, and the older men in his line were regarding him with a rather uneasy eye. Doctors and nurses of the hospital were not supposed to go together, and although Regina gloried in defying all rules, she seems to have observed this one—or he did—for except for glances and hand-holdings behind doors there was apparently nothing more than that between them then. For Regina at that time was many notches above the average girl in understanding, skill and a lot of things. She thought and dreamed on a higher plane, and it was not a pose, either. And here now was this young and promising doctor, who could, if he would, keep her supplied with work, and might even eventually marry her.

"Only the flirtation didn't work out in quite the way she expected. Instead of emotionally 'falling for her,' as she hoped, this very attractive surgeon laid siege in another way, and being repeatedly repulsed he finally left her in a rage, saying he would never return. This was the beginning of the end for Regina—her faith in romance. She stayed in the house day and night for weeks, waiting for her idol to call, sitting by the telephone, walking the floor, crying, raging, fuming—but to no avail. Her pride must have melted some during this ordeal, for finally she called him up to tell him she couldn't live without him.

"If you had known Regina's pride you would realize that this was a bitter pill for her to swallow. Following this came an *affair* which lasted for a number of months—perhaps five or six but not longer. The truth was that her surgeon was not really interested. He was lost in dreams of a career, which ended significantly enough for him, very poorly for her. So all at once she found herself discarded. That is, when she called him up at his office or home, he was not in. Then she took to walking slowly past his office, stopping to play with his dog, or to tie her shoestrings, which somehow always came open just at his place. Also she even began to visit her old hospital in the hope of seeing him, but regularly he managed to avoid her. So far as I know, she never came in contact with him again, even in work.

"In sitting about though, waiting for him to call she had, of course, turned away all cases offered her, and her living then depended entirely upon her earnings. So it was that soon she was being hounded for rent and payments on her furniture. My sister and I offered her shelter in our tiny apartment until she could get her affairs straightened out, but soon it became evident even to our friendly eyes that she had become all but indifferent to life. I think it was during this period that her views of life and of men changed and hardened. There was no least trace of her old air of brisk interest. She seemed to think that we had given her a haven of rest but just the same I think she looked upon us as merely a passing convenience. About this time, that classic: 'You Made Me What I Am To-day, I Hope You're Satisfied,' came out, and we pooled our spare pennies together and bought the record. Regina would hang over it with wet eyes, thinking of her lost *love.*"

We were interrupted at this point and the rest of the story I gathered at odd times. Pieced together, it went something like this:

The two Redmond girls were identified with a form of life which did not countenance the doldrums to any great extent. They were young adventurers, without background or means, as are so many of the thousands who reconnoiter the great cities and without many, if indeed any, severe or wholly unyielding moral scruples. After the brief hours of work in the government bureau with which they were connected, their evenings were devoted to entertainment. Being young and attractive, their place was a rendezvous for certain men of position, all intent upon trips to the theater, card-playing, dancing, dining. It was not long before one of these men, a lobbyist of no little cunning and political notoriety, laid siege to Regina. Neither he nor any of these others was interested in marriage, or even in long-enduring relationships of any kind, but Regina, due to some conventional, or perverse (as such denizens of the middle world might see it) instinct, was interested, if not so much in one life-long love, at least in the complete absorption of one man at one time. So it was that because of some peculiar twist of this man's make-up, his attitude toward women in general, promises he made her, or some hope she had entertained in regard to him which had not been fulfilled, she was of a sudden moved to intense disgust with him. (She was probably undergoing the second great disillusionment of her life.) At any rate at this time she got hold of a revolver and sought to kill him. Having been warned by one of the sisters, he made good his escape, whereupon Regina, rather more than less dissatisfied with life, tried to turn the revolver upon herself. Fortunately or unfortunately as time was to prove, one of her friends interfered and the catastrophe was avoided. But she announced rather coldly that henceforth and forever she was done with men. They should not use her. Instead, she would use them. They should see.

This last decision appears to have led to a material and possibly even mental betterment in her case—for a time, anyhow. For in seeking a way out she decided upon postgraduate courses in chemistry, physiology and bacteriology. And in order to achieve and creditably conclude in these she took herself in hand and did some nursing. Also, she wrote to her father for whom she had no least respect, let alone love, it seems, and begged him for a loan. Much to her astonishment he provided her with a few hundred dollars. Then she came to New York, where she remained two years. When she reappeared in Washington and among her friends for a visit, it was as a postgraduate in her craft, and with the position of superintendent of a small hospital in New York. This position had been secured by application and strictly on merit, and the man whose word carried the most weight was a young physician, Walter La Grange by name. He was the chief consulting physician, as well as the head operating surgeon of the hospital, which, incidentally, he had helped to found.

Because of my intimacy for a period of years with the various members of this group, I came to know La Grange fairly well. He was an interesting example of the cautious, practical medical man, who has had most of his illusions dispelled by his work but still seeks to conform ethically to the tenets of his profession. He was fairly able, I take it;—at least very keen to be identified with all that spelled advance and efficiency in his practice. More, he was pleasing in appearance, courteous, soft spoken—altogether a genial and pleasing type. At that time he lived with his mother and a sister and brother in an old-fashioned brownstone house in the region of Madison Avenue and the Eighties. He had his car, his club, and the various other appendages of those who feel that they are doing very well. But soon after his first meeting with Regina, this quiet tenor of his way was disordered. For, so he confessed to me, later he found himself wishing to be with Regina most of the time. She was, as he said, so brisk, colorful and dynamic—and medically really quite well informed, hence useful to him. Had she been of a different temperament I take it—less inclined to make men pay for the things that had been done to her—it is entirely possible that she and

La Grange would have married. He was the marrying kind.

Not long after the day Regina came to take Miss Redmond for a drive I was casually inducted into an apartment shared by her and this La Grange. Or rather, while not actually a resident, he spent most of his spare daylight and evening hours there. It was a ground-floor suite in one of the few tree-shaded streets in upper Manhattan Island and near the hospital of which La Grange was the chief physician. More, it showed some little taste as to furnishings and ornament. Only and alas one could see that it was a playground of sorts for those who liked a good time. In spite of La Grange and a negro servant, who did this, that and the other all day long, it was evident that house-keeping, and especially cleaning, was done spasmodically. Too often and especially in La Grange's absence the remains of quick and casual lunches, dinners, and midnight suppers were still about the day after. Friends of the type that prefer a helter-skelter, bohemian atmosphere to any other were usually there or just leaving—people of the literary, artistic, and theatrical worlds. Here all sorts of amusing parties were staged. Perhaps too much liquor was consumed on occasion. Perhaps, on occasion, there were certain possibly dangerous tests of the effect of drugs. But without any desire to corrupt any one or to engender a craving which could not be mastered. I thought there was too much talk of the ignorance or unsophistication of others. Too

many people were "dubs," "boobs," "hoi polloi," prole-
tariat," and the like, to suit my taste. But what would
you? Youth will be served. Few of these parties were
ever attended by La Grange. He was too conservative
as well as cautious, perhaps, and appeared to be a little
shy of the social and moral admissions which attendance at affairs of this kind might imply. It is even
possible, as I have often thought since, that he was
not aware of most of them. And at any rate he was sel-
dom to be found there.

But it is not to be assumed from this that Regina
was either indifferent to or neglectful of her hospital
duties or her affectional relations with La Grange,
either. Rather, in regard to him, it was perhaps the dubious or uncertain nature of his general attitude
toward her that caused Regina to suffer and take
refuge in this form of social relief in order to prove
to him that he was in no way master of her moods.
At the same time, although it was long after she
had left the hospital, that I heard this and after her
relations with La Grange had become of a decidedly
different character, it was said by all that she was
the most efficient superintendent the hospital had ever
had. Things moved with quiet and precision. If one
dropped into her sanctum at almost any time, as with
others I sometimes did, it was the usual thing to find
her very much concerned with her affairs, bending over
her desk, giving orders, disposing quickly and definitely
of all sorts of small difficulties. The patient in No. 7 was

not to be given anything but a little milk until to-morrow noon. B operating room was to be prepared at once, all instruments sterilized, Dr. O. to operate. No. 18 might as well be transferred to 6. So she would rattle on. If the visit included an invitation to some affair, and she was interested, she would call a nurse and say: "Miss X., I am going out. Will you take charge of the office? If Dr. K——'s patient arrives, he is to be put in 3. And 10 may have a hypodermic after three, but only in case she doesn't sleep. I will call up or be back by midnight." Then she would throw about her a long, loose blue cape and proceed to her apartment, where, if the occasion demanded, she would make a real toilette. I used to like to look at her as she swung along. She had the air of one who was enjoying life.

But in spite of all this efficiency and gayety, I must say that I personally never quite liked her. She was too evasive, elusive, remote. More, she never seemed to share her confidences with any one. Rather, she preferred to live within herself. If one could trust the accounts of the Redmonds, she was really not a good friend to any one, and in addition, and at bottom, there was something cynical and sinister, and at times even erratic, in all that she did. But in so far as La Grange was concerned, in her personal relations with him, she was said to be strictly loyal and faithful. Yet— and this in spite of her previous experiences, having been so foolish as to compromise herself with him, she was now bent upon winning him to marry her.

This, no doubt, arose from the fact that she had begun to realize that she was growing older, that there was not too much to be said for youthful fire and high jinks, and that he constituted a very respectable and even enviable catch.

Be that as may, presently, or so I heard, she was leading him a dog's life. Among other things, she was becoming jealous and exacting. He could go neither here nor there in such hours as he was free without her knowing all about it, nor could he pay too much attention to his home life if it resulted in any neglect of her. Although this relationship was assumed to be entirely sub rosa, she was not above calling up his home and making inquiries and requests which were likely to prove embarrassing. Nevertheless, he continued to be fond of her, and she never had any real occasion to doubt him. Still, he did not marry her. There were, so I heard, quarrels, brief separations, reunions—the usual rhythm of desire, frustration, opposition, compromise. Apparently each of us—certainly the most of us—as Nietzsche points out, seems to draw a certain kind of success or disaster, about as plants draw a certain kind of insect or a given type of tree the lightning. We have, or are, a fate in ourselves.

It was about this time though, that a new and troublesome element was introduced into Regina's life, and that by herself. She was beginning, so I was told, to experiment with morphine, not because she was depressed or overweighted by her uncertain relations

with La Grange, but more because at heart she was
mischievous or a true rake—one of those bent on
breaking laws and troubling conventions for the fun
of it. Very good—I am prepared to believe that. But
there might well have been some other angle to this
fact. At any rate I have never been satisfied that those
who associated with Regina at the time really understood her. She was too complex, too daring, too different from those about her to be tabulated or pigeon-
holed so readily.

Yet soon, at any rate, morphine had become a regular thing with her. Being superintendent of a hospital
it was plentiful and within her reach. All she had to
do was to take it. Worse, or so I was told, she began
to grow lazy about her work and her clothes,—to
spend too much time in her apartment, asking as an
offset that her assistants call her in case she were
needed. By this time, also, and possibly because of La
Grange's almost nightly absence, she had induced one
of the Redmond girls to come and live with her, and
it is from Marie Redmond that much of all I am
about to relate is gleaned. For Marie it was who explained that in connection with all Regina's hospital
employees and inferiors it was her custom to employ
a high and mighty, if not coldly condescending air.
La Grange, as she pointed out, was her only superior,
and he had sufficient authority to make her rule su-
preme. Just the same, soon after morphine had become
necessary to her, she and La Grange had a quarrel,

(it was assumed by Marie afterward that they had discussed marriage and he had told her he did not want to marry yet), after which Regina proceeded to lock herself in her room, where she remained for a whole day, brooding and injecting morphine into her veins. Returning that evening Marie, as she stated, found the bedroom door locked, whereupon letting herself in through an outside window she discovered Regina prone upon her bed, fully dressed, but in a state of coma, her face and hands of a grayish-brown color. Suspecting morphine and suicide even, her first move was to call for La Grange, who came tearing as fast as his car would bring him. He saw at once what had happened and gave orders that a large pot of strong coffee be brewed, and then, with Marie's aid, as she said, he lifted Regina to her feet, and for sixteen hours these two, together or separately and by turns, walked or half-dragged Regina to and fro, to and fro, until at last some faint signs of consciousness returned. Throughout this mishap, so Marie said, La Grange appeared to be the soul of affectionate distress. Once he gathered Regina into his arms and called to her, asking her why she had done this, assuring Marie it was all due to a misunderstanding, that he really loved Regina and she knew it. More, if she lived, things were to be made different and better for them. He was going to procure a leave of absence for her and together they would take a short vacation. And so they did after she recovered. Also, according to Marie, he appeared to assume that Regina's collapse was due to nothing more than the sudden and rash use of a drug with which she was unfamiliar. Altogether, the immediate effect was to make him more loving. Yet he did not marry her.

And it was then, so I was told, that the vice which later changed her so greatly fastened itself securely upon her. She began to use morphine in such quantities as to rapidly deteriorate a temperament that was apparently vigorous and ambitious. Thus, therefore, whenever she felt despondent or neglected,—or so said Marie—she would go to her room and give herself over to the soothing lethargy induced by the drug. At such times a ring of the doorbell or the telephone meant nothing to her. Both were either disconnected or ignored, and it was assumed by all, even La Grange, that she was out. Apart from noting that she was more irritable than before her attempt at suicide, La Grange, so said Marie, appeared to think nothing of it. She was still reasonably active and competent in the prosecution of her duties, and to a certain extent interested in pleasure. In fact, according to Marie, it was much over a year before La Grange began to guess that there was something radically wrong with Regina. Previous to that her noticeable periods of unusual gayety and affection, punctuated by moods of peculiar indifference, appeared to deceive him. He did not appear to sense the grip that the drug already had on her. Always neat and rather proud of her appearance, it was only with the lapse or a year that she began to idle about her apartment, and even the hospital, in none too well-laundered uniforms. Her hair, as I was told, no longer received the care which previously had been indicated by various tasteful arrangements of it.

But conjointly with all this would also come sudden changes of mood, during which she would develop an almost inordinate zeal for cleanliness—possibly an offset to her previously ill-balanced actions. At such times, though, she joined these cleanliness bursts with the privilege of calling up various smart Fifth Avenue shops and ordering many things sent for her inspection. With little regard for expense, either to herself or La Grange, she would then retain many of them, charging them either to herself or him and soon, according to my confidant, her trunks and closets were actually stuffed with beautiful but useless things, which later she would give away or sell for little or nothing. Always liberal with her to the extent of his means, La Grange at first said nothing, but later, certain of her purchases appearing to him to be too extravagant, he ventured to question her. Her answer was that he did not have to pay for anything if he did not wish to. A quarrel, followed by her disappearance for a few days, was the only result.

Later, however, resenting additional questioning by La Grange, and being still in the mood for these expenditures, she now proceeded to borrow from the hospital cash drawer. That is, changing some of the

amounts received on different occasions, she pocketed
the difference, trusting to her salary and the generosity of La Grange at the end of the month to be able to
make up the abstracted amounts. And for a long time
this she was able to do, a balancing and auditing of her
books by the directors occurring but once every three
months. In fact, I myself was once called upon to
make a temporary advance so that her books might
balance, but in about ten days this was returned, she
having possibly taken it from the cash drawer again.

Be that as it may, on one occasion she was not so
able to make her balance without an immediate and
large advance. Since La Grange was the only person
from whom such a sum could be obtained quickly
and easily, she was, perforce, compelled to appeal to
him. Again, a protest from him, so I heard, and then in
a fit of temper she defiantly told him that she had taken
the money from the cash drawer. This was sufficient
to horrify La Grange, whose feeling for economic and
financial order was so great as to cause him to immediately replace the sum, though not without another appeal to Regina for reform. This so irritated her as to
cause her without an explanatory word to resign her
place and depart for Washington, where, taking quarters in a hotel and resorting to her favorite relief, morphine, a goodly amount of which she had filched from
the hospital, she remained for days. Having had
enough of being alone, she finally visited one of her
group then in Washington, one, by the way, with

whom La Grange had already been in communication in the hope of finding some trace of her. This girl, seeing Regina's gloomy and distrait condition, wired La Grange, whereupon he went to her. What promises, if any, were made on this occasion are not known, but she returned with him and with his help resumed her work at the hospital.

But, according to all, by this time she had lost interest in her work, and, to a certain extent, in La Grange even. He did not understand her, so Marie said she complained, once. Also that all men were fools or cowards or worse. At any rate by then life appeared to have lost its salt. She was apparently permanently depressed or indifferent and returned by degrees to her old foolish expenditures and petty defalcations. Yet, instead of indulging in parties as of yore now she began to retire early and lie abed late. Hospital work no longer interested her, and she began to shirk it. When she did appear there, it was usually in a costume unpleasantly suggestive of one profoundly indifferent to appearances. She seemed to sleep at her desk; at times, to be in a kind of stupor. Whispers and then complaints went around. And finally when an inquiry was suggested by one of the other doctors, and La Grange mentioned it to her, she chose again to resign, this time for good. Thereafter, she took to her bed and announced that she was ill. La Grange endeavored to make her confess to her habit, so that he might send her to a sanitarium, but she would not admit it and would not take the cure. It is perhaps at this time that his affection for her began to lose its original force. He was not seen at her apartment quite so much, although he still sought, in every way, to make her life as comfortable as before. As always, upon a word from her he would come and take her for a drive, to dinner, or to the theater. But, in the main, as he later said, she appeared to wish to moon and drift, and he could do nothing with her.

And then occurred one of those encounters most calculated to arouse the jealousy of any woman. She once saw La Grange with another woman, either in a restaurant or a theater, I cannot now recall. As it turned out, the girl was a young and attractive relative visiting his family, but the incident was sufficient to bring on a dark and disturbing scene. She called up his home and wanted to know, (and from his sister, who chanced to answer the telephone), where and with whom he was. Miss La Grange had never heard of Regina, and was probably astonished at the wild and authoritative tone. At any rate, she asked who was inquiring, and why. Answer—Regina C——. Also that she had every right to know. The sister refused any information on the ground that she did not know anything about the person calling.

The effect of this was even more disturbing. The one thing that La Grange did not wish his family, (his mother, especially, of whom he was very fond), to know was that he was conducting this clandestine affair. His mother, so he confessed to Marie, had always thought that when the time came he would marry a girl in his own world, in an open and socially conforming way. And had he ever married Regina it would have been in this manner, so as to place her on a level with himself. But now he chose to look upon this latest action of hers as a breach in that solid wall of respectability which must eventually surround her and him if they were to be married at all. When he called her the next morning to explain and protest, he found that she was already the worse for the drug that he feared. She was in a half stupor, and when aroused was in no way repentant for what she had done. Rather, she deluged him with accusations of indifference and deception, which he could only deny, but she would not believe him. She asked him why she should care what his mother or family thought. What did they care for her? Let him give some thought to her condition socially and otherwise.

It was from this time that La Grange began to manifest an indifference toward her which most certainly hurried that despair which brought about the end. All reasonable bills were paid—rent, food, clothes. His car was at her command. Whenever she called for him he would come, but he did not call as frequently and as voluntarily as he had. Neither did he, or perhaps would he, understand how any one could so completely lose hold of herself and life because of a disappointment in the matter of the affections. Perhaps he was not one who could grasp the depth and destroying force of some women's affections. Be that as it may the result of this was that she resorted more and more to her principal resource against ennui and regret —morphine. According to her friends, she had taken a very large supply from the hospital and hidden it in a nearby safety vault. When this supply was gone, she sought to buy more, but just then as it chanced one of those periodic and sharp campaigns was being waged against all doctors and druggists who provided prescriptions too freely, and morphine was not easy to obtain. Yet Regina, being a vigorous and executive person, especially when pressed by any such need as this, now bestirred herself. By this time the drug seemed to have weakened or set at naught any inhibitive scruples that she might have possessed.

For instance, she bethought her that an ample supply was always to be found in the drug-room of her former hospital. Dressing herself in her best one day, she revisited that institution, explaining on her arrival that she had been away from the city for some time and naturally was very curious as to the condition of the old place and had come merely to look it over. Might she? She would just walk about without putting anybody to the trouble of showing her around. The superintendent who knew at least something of her ability and former power smiled blandly and turned her over to a nurse to be shown about. But Regina, coming to the floor where the drug-room was, requested the nurse

in attendance to get her something and in her absence
hurried to the room. It was locked, to be sure, but she
had retained a key. Opening the door she seized from
the spot where it had always stood the bottle containing the hospital's supply, then closed it and returned
to the office and her attendant and the new superintendent, to both of whom she later bade farewell.
Later, learning from La Grange how the mysterious
theft was discovered, and the lock on the drug-room
door changed, she felt free to relate her ruse to Marie.
Himself completely fooled La Grange later also related
this remarkable happening to Marie, not suspecting
Regina until long afterwards, and then solely because
she herself derisively related how easy it had been to
hoodwink him and all.

But tricky and dangerous as this was, (involving
liability to arrest for theft), it was as nothing compared
to other shifts which now followed. One of these related to La Grange himself. Like all doctors he was
in the habit of carrying a hypodermic outfit in the inside pocket of his coat, but to get this case was her
problem. Chemically trained, Regina knew that strychnia pills look almost like those of morphia; only a
very careful examination of them side by side could
reveal the difference. The thing to do then, when she
needed morphine, was to induce La Grange to take
off his coat, and then express a sudden wish for something in the kitchen. This challenge accepted, and the
coat left, it was an easy matter to rifle the case of its

phial and the phial of at least some of its pellets, the same replaced with strychnia so as to avoid detection. The fact that because of this exchange another's life might be endangered had come to mean nothing to Regina. Life! Bunk! What about her own life? Did any one care for that? Assuming, though, that this ruse failed, as sometimes it did and there was another present whom she could interest, she would invite La Grange to show the unsophisticated third person the method by which patients were relieved of pain. If the case were produced and she could lay hands on the phial, so as to show the uninitiated how much she knew about such things, it was not difficult to uncork the bottle and spill two, or three, or four, on the floor unnoticed, the same later to be gathered up. I am not troubling to add additional instances since these will suffice.

Just the same these tricks were said to have been worked by her at least a dozen times during the course of the second year. Naturally, since La Grange was not always at her disposal these same had to be supplemented by others. One of these, as I now recall, related to a girl who had once come to the hospital over which Regina presided and had there been treated for the very habit of which she was now a victim. Suspecting that she had never been completely cured, Regina now sought her out. Her plan, as it proved, was to strike up an alliance with her by which both might come by the means of their mutual undoing. As fate would have it, this particular girl was open to, and even anxious for, just such an alliance. Between them then and therefore they hatched a workable plan. The girl was to go to bed pretending to be ill and a doctor sent for, Regina for the time being posing as a trained nurse employed by the patient. The doctor having arrived, a desperate case of gallstones was alleged. In the face of groans and much artistically simulated misery by the patient, it was not out of order for the nurse to suggest a hypodermic. But the doctor starting for the kitchenette to sterilize the needle and prepare the drug, Regina's plan was to come forward and with an ingratiating smile exclaim, in her best Southern manner: "Oh, no, doctor, yo' can't go in theah! The kitchen is too mussy. I wouldn't have you see it fo' worlds. Let me go, Ahm, ah, a trained nurse, yo' know, and can do it fo' yo'." A smile, a profound air of sincerity, and the doctor returned to the patient, whose condition became noticeably worse at the moment. In the kitchen the phial was rifled of its contents and strychnia substituted, an injection given the patient, and the doctor dismissed.

This was a mere preliminary to a long series of hoaxes. Together they remembered a nurse who was in attendance upon a number of rich patients who were addicted to the drug habit. It was assumed by them that she must have morphine in her possession, and upon her they now descended. Their call was in the guise of a social visit, and soon they were engaged in reminiscent patter. In the midst of this, though, Regina, who was really the active agent in all this, asked for the privilege of rearranging her hair. Escorted to the only bedroom of her hostess and left there, her confederate resumed the interrupted talk. No sooner was the door closed though than Regina went through every piece of clothing, every box, bag, casket, drawer in the room and also searched the closet in a connecting bathroom. As a blind, (the details are all Marie's, gathered from Regina or her friends at different times), she let down her hair and went about carrying a brush in one hand. But the search remaining unrewarded and her stay being unduly prolonged, the nurse was about to come to the door to see if there was anything her guest needed when a ring of the telephone bell interfered and she paused to attend to that. Thereupon the confederate hastened to warn Regina of the impending danger, and the following conversation is said to have taken place:

"For God's sake, come on! I can't think of another thing to say! And she's coming in here. She had already started when the telephone rang."

"Oh," plaintively from Regina, "I've looked everywhere and haven't been able to find a thing. But . . . but . . ." and this with an illumined gleam of the eye, "I haven't looked there," and she dived desperately toward an overlooked shoe-drawer at the bottom of a built-in wardrobe. This time she emerged triumphant, a full tube of morphine in her hand. She now proceeded to the mirror, volubly and loudly explaining how very difficult it was to do anything with her hair these days. In a moment she was in the other room, pattering about how grateful she was for this courtesy and what a charming and livable suite it was. In a few moments more both were bidding their hostess an affectionate farewell.

But even this was as nothing. A certain Mary K——, a Washington nurse who had known Regina there and was now living in New York, met her on the street and foolishly accepted an invitation to call. Instantly, Regina began a fictitious account of her own active practice, her many patients, and, what was more, (the great European war being then in full swing), how many charity patients she had—wounded ex-soldiers— to whom she was giving as much of her time as possible. This Mary had once met one of the Redmond sisters, and Regina to further her plans in connection with her now began a most moving account of the dreadful disaster that had befallen a brother of the Redmonds. He had come back from the war wounded about the face and stomach. Partial blindness and cancer of the stomach had followed. The cure of either ailment was out of the question. All that could possibly be done for the shambling, suffering, and disjointed soul was to give him morphine to relieve his intense and constant pain. As Regina told it death was a mere matter of months, at best. His sisters were devoted to him and were doing everything they could, but since that drug was now so scarce as well as expensive to come by, three or four injections a day being necessary, they were finding it an almost intolerable expense. She herself had given a great deal; but was at a loss now as to where to get more. Perhaps she, Mary, would be glad to help. Wouldn't she? Couldn't she? If only she would!

Mary was of a sober and conscientious turn, not one given to trifling with the law or the ethics of her profession. Just how could she, was her thoughtful and dubious reply.

"Well," went on her newly-encountered friend, "you could get him some morphine, couldn't you? I know it's against the rules, but in a case like this——"

The story sounded plausible enough. Beginning by protesting that she could not think of doing anything so unprofessional, she finally veered to where she agreed to supply a few pills at least, enough for a week's need. Fearing a change of heart, Regina accompanied her to her rooms in order to be sure of them.

This supply exhausted, though, there arose the question of how to obtain more. For by now Regina's unscrupulous daring had already frightened off her erstwhile confederate, and she was working alone. Yet even so, according to those who knew her, there was no source of supply that she was willing to relinquish this side of exposure and arrest. Being sorely pressed one night, not so very long after, she again called up that same Mary K—— and began a supplement to the preceding tale. First, of course, there was a long and grateful introduction concerning the good that had been accomplished by Mary's gift. The patient, while no better, of course, was suffering less, and his sister had been relieved of the dreadful expense of having a doctor in three or four times a day, she, (Regina), having taught her how to use the needle. But now the morphine was all gone and it was necessary that more be obtained. Regina herself had just been to see them and had given them all she had, enough for the day at least, but she could do no more. Would not this new benefactor come to the rescue once more? It would be a real charity.

This time while generously sympathetic Mary was more practical. She was not unwilling to go farther in this matter but insisted upon seeing the patient. It was as she explained much too unethical to be handing out drugs unless one knew the conditions surrounding the patient. Couldn't she come and see Marie and her brother? For once the schemer was nonplused, but only for a moment.

"Why, yes, of course, to be sure. Only, I forgot. Marie is taking him to the country in the morning for a few days. Some friends of mine are coming for him in their car. And his condition is very bad tonight. I don't think it would be advisable to disturb him."

"Maybe I could get around before they go," insisted Mary. "What time are they leaving in the morning?"

"Why, yes, that is possible. Only they are leaving at

nine, and I didn't tell you where they are living now, did I?"—and she gave an address as far as possible from the region in which Mary dwelt.

It was rather difficult, and Mary gave over, seeing that insisting implied a doubt of her friend's veracity. She grudgingly gave her another week's supply, and then, feeling that she had awakened suspicion, Regina did not trouble her again. And it was not until Mary met Marie Redmond on the street a year later that the truth came out.

Next came a second offense against the ethical sense of La Grange which as related to me by Marie who had it direct from Regina some weeks later went as follows. Throughout all this period as Marie explained to me the relationship between Regina and La Grange had never been quite broken. He was still her good and best friend—sympathetic, tolerant, helpful. On occasions he saw her and, of course, was wholly unaware of her present quite desperate and wholly criminal course. From time to time during the period as well as before and all unknown to him, his morphine phial was rifled and filled with strychnia. But there came a day once when for seventy-two hours, and for all her resourcefulness and artifice, Regina was unable to secure a "shot." La Grange therefore stood forth as her one resource. He must be persuaded to visit her and she must rob his phial. Driven by her great need she began calling him up one night after midnight, and at his home. Wouldn't he come to her? She was so very ill. Her standard complaint recently—nerves —was driving her insane. She must have something, a dose of morphine, to quiet her. "But, Regina," he is said to have answered, reprovingly, "you know I won't do anything like that. Let me send you some chloral or somnal." "No, no, no!" she almost screamed. Unless something were done, and quickly, she would do something desperate—kill herself and have it over with.

This brought him, as Marie said, and at once. He found her in genuine distress, walking the floor, wringing her hands and begging for relief. Convinced at last of her need he took out his hypodermic case and proceeded to sterilize the needle by the aid of an alcohol flame. Suddenly she stopped in her walking and as if just then recalling something, exclaimed: "Oh, no, no! Wait, Walter! That . . . that isn't morphine. I forgot."

"Not morphine?" he inquired.

"No," she said. "It's strychnia."

He paused, puzzled, and then as though he were on the track of something, added:

"What makes you think it's strychnia?"

"Because one day here, not so long ago when you went to the store for me I took out your case . . . just to look at it . . . and in fooling with it I spilled all the pills down the washstand there. And then I thought you might be angry, and so I put strychnia back in their place. I thought you might be angry . . ."

"So!" he replied, sitting down. "I see. You . . . you didn't use any of the morphine, by chance?"

"No, of course not. How can you say that to me? Of course, I didn't use any."

For answer La Grange sat there. This was the revelation he had long feared. The professional laxity, or dishonesty, or ethical deterioration which had permitted such a development as this was too much for him. He was disgusted, and from then on did his best to separate himself from one whom he no longer considered ethically responsible. But on this occasion, because of the state she was in, he went and secured morphia and gave her a dose, at the same time making it plain that he would no longer favor her in that way. She must either submit to treatment and cure, if she was an addict, (which she still denied), or she must look to others for her supply.

But if he was done with Regina she was not done with him, even though she realized that her hold upon him had withered to a dry and colorless claim. Due perhaps to the influence of the drug, she later declared to one of the Redmond sisters that she hated him and would see to it that he was punished for the way he was treating her. Had he not had the best of her love and devotion, and now see. Once about this time, according to Marie, she even outlined a plan by which she could take a deadly revenge if she but chose. She would have him drive her out to some lonely spot in the woods, or a park, where she would shoot herself with his revolver, which he kept in his car. Thus she would leave him to explain all. With no witnesses, his weapon, and with herself, the only one who could clear him, dead, she was sure that he would end in the electric chair! Another plan was to kill herself on his mother's doorstep, leaving a letter which would explain why she had done it. But these were the dreams of one lost in the fumes of a drug.

At that time, also, as it chanced, a goodly number of women with twisted lives, and some whose lives were not so twisted, were looking to the war and France to either regenerate or restore them, spiritually and in other ways, or to do for them entirely. Hundreds were setting forth on that adventure, so why not Regina? Besides there was great public interest in as well as homely sympathy and generosity for those who were going abroad. Regina, sensing this, perhaps, lost no time in taking advantage of it. Visiting an old druggist from whom as superintendent of a hospital she had purchased many supplies, she explained to him how, now, she was going to France as a war nurse. It was her patriotic duty. But, alas, as she also explained, she was without funds. The druggist, recalling her as an old and liberal customer and in his turn, responding to the call of his country, grandiosely announced that she might take everything she needed and there would be no charge. Certainly he could do that much for his country if girls like Regina were going to help nurse the wounded. Thus encouraged, she at once proceeded to select the various things she might be supposed to need, (but which were actually supplied by the government), only in the midst of her labors she suddenly stopped and came to the crux of her visit.

"Oh . . . ah . . . Doctor Kaye, I just now remember. I haven't any drugs, and I hear that they are very scarce over there. It would be a good idea if I took some with me. Could you . . . ah . . . let me have some . . ." and here followed a list of four or five things, winding up with: "and some morphine, too? I hear that there is a great shortage of that."

Mr. Kaye was a little disturbed. For regularly those days his place was visited by inspectors from various bureaus, city, state and national. The war on habit-forming drugs was growing very sharp. At once therefore he began to apologize, saying that he could not possibly give her any without a doctor's prescription, whereupon Regina at once assumed a very injured air. Was she not a trained nurse and until recently—before deciding to go to war, in charge of a hospital? How little he understood either her or her purpose or motives and so proceeded toward the door. Whereupon the druggist weakened, defeated by her tactics, and so apologized, and proceeded to supply her with thirty grains, exacting in return, however, a promise from her to safeguard him in so far as the law was concerned. With this windfall she was at peace for another week or so.

Yet shortly after this she actually did embark for France, where she remained for some seven months.

Whether she went as a nurse, or served as an efficient one or not was never truly learned. For the period of her service, though, it was necessary for her to assign to another her nurse's salary. Believing as she did—or so Marie said that she would never come back alive, she generously proceeded to make over this sum of thirty dollars a month to Marie as the one person who had been most kind to her. (She had entirely cut herself off from her family and Marie was really her only friend.) Nothing was heard of her by Marie until some seven months later, when suddenly she reappeared, or rather wrote from a third-rate hotel in New York, where apparently she was lying ill. According to the story of Marie, who took her the accumulated checks she had retained unused, she was living in a very shabby room, the blinds drawn throughout the day, herself wandering about in a soiled brown sweater and nightgown. By then much of her beauty was gone, and this loss was all the more emphasized by the indifference with which she regarded her person. Cigarette butts and ashes and burnt matches littered the floor and bed. A pack of well-thumbed cards, with which she played solitaire or told her fortune, lay upon a table.

According to Marie, who had it from Regina herself, she had already telephoned La Grange, who apart from one visit, during which he gave her some money, had not been sufficiently interested to renew the relationship. Rather, as she said, he had urged her to take treatment for her vice and undertake some active employment, but she had refused both suggestions since, as she said, "life was no longer worth it." Incidentally she had built up a large bill at the hotel, to the liquidation of which she refused to apply any of the money returned by Marie. The hotel didn't need it as much as she did. But being still in uniform and the sympathy of the stay-at-homes still at fever heat for those returning she was not bothered. Subsequently she slipped away, leaving her trunk.

To this Marie added: "I saw that she was too far gone for me to help her. I had nothing myself, and the mere sight of her made me very unhappy, really terrified me. I had a feeling that I might in some way be taken with the virus of indifference and failure, that was afflicting her, and so avoided her thereafter. It was really fear that kept me away. And still I could not help admiring her for some of the things she had accomplished in the past."

But this was not the end, either. From another quarter of the city, and quite some little time later she was again heard of, and in a rather dramatic way. Having at one time come in contact with a girl of rather loose morals who occupied a small apartment in one of those poorly reputed buildings which adjoin the negro section of upper Manhattan Island, she had moved into this same building. Here, with nothing more than a suitcase, a pallet, and a store box for bureau, she lived for a few months, preserving, however, her nurse's uniform and cap, which she found useful in her quest for morphine. All of her other former belongings, which had been placed in storage when she went abroad, had either been sold or lost for non-payment of dues. Just the same, she either could not or would not work, and seemed for the time being content to let La Grange go.

It was in this room, though, where she lay all day long with blinds drawn that she concocted a new ruse. This was to array herself in her uniform, and satchel in hand, call at any hospital where either the doctors or nurses were known to her by name. Arriving at the office of the superintendent, she would announce that she had been retained as a private nurse for a patient, but then being brought or sent in by one of the doctors, both doctor and patient presumably being on the way. And might she be allowed to wait in the office, adjoining which was usually the drug-room? Quieted usually by her assured and confident manner, the superintendent and nurses would come and go without paying any attention to her. The moment the room in which she was chanced to be empty, though, she would dash into the drug-room, if it chanced to be open, and rifle it of whatever morphine it might contain. Immediately afterwards, whether successful or not, she would tell whosoever came into the room that she had changed her mind and would wait at the entrance for the doctor, and so, of course, make her escape.

But on one of these expeditions, as it turned out,

and by a nurse who knew her to be a stranger, she was
espied emerging from the drug-room. Before she could
escape, she was stopped, interrogated, and then
searched. At first—so the newspaper accounts ran, she
indignantly denied taking any drugs, but the search
yielding a goodly amount of morphine, she was detained, and then fell silent—made no comment of any
kind. Of course, she was held and informed that unless
she could bring forward friends who would vouch for
her, she would be turned over to the police. Giving a
fictitious name and address, she now sent telegrams to
various fictitious persons out of town, presumably in
order to gain time. Pending response to these, she was
placed in a second-floor room which looked out upon
a stone court, and a nurse placed in charge of her. Here
she remained from ten o'clock in the morning until late
in the evening, no answer to any of her messages coming, of course. About dinner time, though, she pleaded
faintness from hunger and asked that something be
given her. Moved by sympathy, the nurse in charge of
her went into the hall to call another nurse either to
take charge of her patient or to bring the food, whereupon when she returned again it was just in time to see
Regina's feet going over the window ledge. She was attempting to clear a wall which enclosed the court, and
gave into an open lot some ten feet below which adjoined the hospital. And she would have cleared it and
might have made good her escape had it not been that
her dress caught on a hook outside the window. This

threw her to the ground below, breaking both of her wrists and otherwise injuring her. Just the same the police were notified and she was incarcerated in the detention ward of the hospital until she should be able to appear in court.

Meanwhile, the case attracting considerable newspaper publicity, photographs were published, and although a false name had been given, still Marie, La Grange and others knew who it was. Moved by her plight, La Grange investigated and sought to secure her release. By this time, however, she had been taken in hand by an emotional woman philanthropist conducting a home for erring girls on the East Side, and this woman, with the permission of the court, removed her to that institution, where she remained for some time. It was here that La Grange came to rebreak and reset her wrists, improperly set in the first place. Later he secured her discharge as cured, and later still La Grange and her woman philanthropist friend, testifying in her behalf, the case against her was dismissed. For some time thereafter, so it was said, La Grange contributed to her support. However, her mood toward life being by now hopeless, a craving for the drug soon returned, and she disappeared and was heard of only twice afterward.

On one of these occasions, so Marie Redmond said, she came to her and announced that she was living in a basement room in one of the poorer sections of the city. To explain her emaciated appearance she said she had not been well, but now she was going to work. She was through with drugs and had just secured a nursing case in New Haven—some man, or agency, that knew of her nursing ability having recommended her to a patient there, but she lacked carfare. Would Marie advance her the money? She would be met at the train and provided for thereafter, if only she could get the fare. This was given her, as well as a bag, a dress and a hat, because as Marie said the things she was wearing were unbelievably shabby. None the less, and so late as all this and after all her desperate life, Marie described her as standing before her mirror in her new finery, preening and twisting and turning to see how she looked. "I'm not so bad even now," was what Marie said she said, and later Marie added on her own account, and addressing me, of course, "She, who had had her evening dresses and her satin slippers, and who had walked with the air of one fully conscious of the attention she was certain to attract! And that in the face of the fact that the things in which she was studying herself were a mess—cast-off things which I was ashamed to offer, but which were all I had to give her at the time."

Four days later, though, she was again back and with another story. She had gone to New Haven, true enough, but on her arrival found no one to meet her. (She had not bothered to ask the name of the patient she was bound for.) Night was coming on and she had no money to return. What to do? Witness a flash of her old spirit and invention! She registered at a hotel, bathed, had dinner sent up, and after a good night's rest, her breakfast, for which she signed checks. After breakfast, restored by this excellent treatment, she wandered about the streets, endeavoring to think of some way out. Presto, a gentleman, of the type that always responds to intelligence and culture, to whom she explained her plight. And at once he gave her sufficient to meet her hotel bill, to pay her way back to New York, and to leave a balance sufficient for her to live on for a little while. In proof of which, if you please, she returned the loan and bag to Mary, and departed, returning in a few weeks to say that she had written her new lover for aid and that he had sent her—believe it or not—two hundred dollars. Whether this was true or not, her personal appearance was considerably improved. She left, and was never again seen by Marie.

But once again after that even she heard of her, and in a most peculiar way. For it appears that La Grange, who had remained on terms of friendship with the Redmond sisters for some time after Regina and all connected with her had passed out of his life, one day called on or perhaps encountered one or the other of them and on this occasion related how some time back his attention and charity had been called to the case of a girl in very great need of an operation, and with no money to pay for it, but by no less a person than Regina herself. For old sake's

sake, as Marie said he phrased it, he promised to operate on the girl and ordered her to appear at a certain
hospital. What was his astonishment when, going to
the hospital and to the girl's room, he found Regina
there, and in an immaculate uniform, and in charge of
the case, or so she had told the superintendent. And
now, owing to some freak or weakness of mind, she
was pretending that the old affectional relationship
between herself and La Grange still existed. He was
her Wally, and she proceeded thus to address him,
beaming upon him in a most loving manner. What to
do? He could either face it out and as delicately as possible evade her, or he could have her ejected from the
hospital, in which case it was possible that a scene and
complications might have ensued. He chose, therefore,
as he said, to humor her to some extent, making jests
and evasive replies, but cautioning the patient and
house nurse who had been assigned to the case to be on
their guard against any proffers of service. She was
finally removed from the case on the ground that he
was going out of town and that another doctor who
had nurse favorites of his own was to take charge.
Before going he again gave her money, but he never
saw her again.

That, in so far as I know, was the end of the story,
except for the following, written me some two years
later by Marie, to whom I had appealed:

"No, I have never heard anything more about
Regina, and I don't believe that anybody else has.

It might be that she recovered her sanity and poise and resumed some form of normal life, but I doubt it. She was too far gone. A nurse whom we both knew told me only a few months ago that a girl descriptively answering to Regina had been picked up unconscious on the street and taken to Bellevue. When consciousness returned she proved to be raving mad and was transferred to Central Islip, a derelicts' asylum, I believe, where she died in a straitjacket. I wrote there, but they informed me that no one answering to that description had either been brought or died there recently. Dr. La Grange also tells me that he has gone over all of the records at Bellevue and Central Islip, and that there is no proof that Regina was ever there. He seems to wish to believe that she is alive, but that may be because it would bother his conscience to believe her dead. Yet the Lord knows he did all he could for her—more than most men would have done.

"I should add that another girl has still more recently told me that she either saw or thought she saw Regina on the street here, and that she looked prosperous and happy. But I don't believe it. Some months ago another nurse said that she had had a letter from her in Denver, but nobody else ever saw the letter. Another is supposed to have seen her in Washington, looking very well. But I have never seen nor heard from her since she came to me two years ago, and I figure that if she were alive and well off she would scarcely hide away from everybody who knew her, and if she were alive and poor, she would certainly have appealed to me or some of the others who have known her. I was about the only one toward the last to whom she seemed to feel she could come without danger of criticism, but I have never heard a thing. My guess is, she's dead."

And so it may be. Personally I have always been inclined to think of her as a capable but erratic soul, one who had some queer twist in regard to the affections and who seemed to think that unless life could be bent to her mood it was not worth living, or at least not worth working for. Wherever she is, let us hope that the next scheme of things will be more to her taste.

But as for La Grange—well, he is still unmarried. He lives with his brother. His mother is dead, his sister married.

RELLA

Foreword

THIS story, innately truthful and self-revealing, was outlined to me one evening in Greenwich Village many years ago by an American poet who has since died; and before him by his wife and the girl to whom he referred. Since no names appear, and his quondam fame, as well as name, has dimmed with time, there can be, to me, no conceivable reason why the sketchy transcript I made of it then should not now be enlarged upon according to the mood in which he related it to me.

—THE AUTHOR

Rella

❦❦ ❦❦

"Whenever I think of Rella I think of a backwoods state such as Arkansas. Those round knobs and tumbled earthen breakers called the Ozarks; the great fields of wheat and corn and oats amid which her young life was laid; the tumbling, sparkling rill of a stream which ran diagonally across a corner of the large farm owned by her father; and the fine upstanding trees and tumultuous spread of wild flowers all about. Great argosies of woolly clouds sailed the heavens in summer and gave rise to dreams of blue seas and white sails. From the fields came the whirr of the reaper, the call of many farmhands employed for the harvesting, the lowing of cattle and the bleat of sheep.

"Her father, Samuel Howdershell, was a successful farmer as well as a politician of sorts. At least he had contrived to secure from the leaders of his party the position of United States marshal which occupied but a small portion of his time. When he was not able to look after his farm in person, the shrewd and talkative little woman who was his wife, and who obviously liked the world in which she found herself, was there to do it for him. And she did it with a will and with skill, assisted by her two ruddy and vigorous sons, who seemed to look upon her as their guide and mentor.

In winter they were away at school, as was the girl about whom I am writing.

"But the air of smartness that went with their apparel in that far-away region—the something of city manners and city tastes! Automobiles were few in those days, but each of the Howdershell children had a riding horse. And the large barn sheltered several polished conveyances as well as the farming machinery which equipped so large a farm; also the immense crops of hay and corn which were reaped from the fields. Indeed, Howdershell had an office in the barn, in which he kept his papers and books, also a typewriter which either his wife or one of the children operated when necessary. Then there were parties and regional affairs of considerable importance to which the ordinary run of native farmers and their folk were not invited but of which the family of a United States marshal was an integral and respected part. In short, these people moved in a busy, genial, sociable world, which at that far-from-happy period in my own life impressed me as particularly blessed and fortunate.

"I was married at the time—presumably happily married. And yet, the truth was that at thirty, and only two years married, I had begun to realize that for me marriage was a mistake. Either mine was not a temperament which lent itself to marriage, or I had erred in selecting the mate with whom it might have proved a success. Being young and far this side of an adequate conception of the mysteries of life and the harsh com-

pulsions of society and the state, which invariably seek
to preserve themselves at the expense of the individual,
I was at a loss to understand my predicament. Perhaps I was suffering for my early ignorance and folly.
But the laws of society were immutable, of course.
Once married, always married . . . 'Whom God hath
joined together, let no man put asunder.' . . . These
and similar decrees and ordinances and injunctions of
our derived society haunted me like the voice of fate.
From every tree and bush, to say nothing of the ordinary palaver of the home and the street, came voices
to say that even the dark whisperings within me were
wrong, very wrong; and yet about me, gay with temp-
tation, were youth and love at play. Who would take
me by the hand and lead me forth from that slough
of despond? Whither—whither—from the great urge
within that gave me no rest? Those who know nothing
of the love of beauty that walks hand in hand with
passion will never understand. To them the mysteries
remain the mysteries.

"However, being young, I could not but hope against
hope. I had just had a play accepted and was writing
poems and stories and getting them published—finding
myself, as it were. My wife, as I could plainly see, was
pluming herself on the fact that I had a future and
that she was to share in it in an interesting way. But,
as I often thought, she was entitled, certainly, to all
the joy that life might bring her. On the other hand,
here was this union which for me could only end in

beclouding my life, however much sunshine it might result in for her. Was I to work, work, work, and share all with one who could only be an annoyance and a weariness to me? And yet, this very thought, at that time, seemed to me the very substance of evil. Ought one not, rather, crucify oneself upon the cross of duty, charity, sympathy? Ought one not? I went about brooding over my lot, wondering almost hourly what was to become of me. And in so doing I could only marvel at this mystery of love. For here was a girl— my wife—as attractive physically as any of those about me—and yet, after two years and for, to me, some almost inexplicable reason, meaning less to me than almost any other. Her ways! I knew them all. Most of her moods and views, apart from her ultra-conventional ones, interested me, but she did not. And this was the same girl who only a year or two before had seemed to me to be the all-desirable. Let him explain who can!

"And yet, because of sympathy for her and self-condemnation for what I considered an unconscionable vagary in myself to which no well-constructed individual would think of giving way, I had in no way indicated my change of mood. And in so far as I could judge, she had no inkling of it. Yet, in spite of this, let any one of her friends—women, the attractive ones, especially—conduct themselves in any but the most formal way about me, and she was off upon a lecture which concerned the compulsions and moral safe-

guards of the married state. Her chief social desire,
apparently, was to know whether the men and women
of her circle were morally, and hence socially, sound
and pure. And however dull and uninteresting the
sound ones might be, they were infinitely to be preferred to those who were not. At least they were good
people. To the end of establishing this fact, therefore,
she studied all and sundry, with a view to weeding out
the unfit.

"And yet, when it came to the world at large, realizing that there were degrees of talent and that by
some queer twist of life the morally unsatisfactory too
often provided whatever flare and color the visible
social scene might have, she was inclined to study
the successful and the beautiful, unmoral or what you
will, and from them to copy such nuances of style
and manner, and thought, even—where it did not con-
flict with her own convictions—as would serve to
heighten her own charm. And by the same token,
those who were decidedly moral, but at the same time
not smart and not so well-placed socially or financially
as some others, were not, apart from certain safe contacts she was inclined to court, likely to attract her
interest. This self-protective cleverness, however admirable it might appear to some, did little more than
puzzle and at times irritate me. Her idea, as I was beginning to see—or thought I was—was to strengthen
herself by such arts as these evil ones might suggest

without at the same time contaminating herself or her blissful married state.

"But all the while I was miserably restless and unhappy, and daily becoming more so, constantly contemplating in my mind's eye what I considered to be the happier love states of others. And envying them their bliss. Oh, youth, youth, youth! Beauty! The scorching lure of it! Without the favor of some gloriously beautiful girl, as I reasoned, I might as well be dead! But at the same time I was convinced that being married, no woman, young or old, good, bad or indifferent, would have anything to do with me! Least of all one such as at this time could have filled the frame of my fancy. Had I been more assured—less convinced of my own conclusion—some rather obvious indications or proofs to the contrary might have swayed me—but I was not.

"It was June of a lovely summer that found us visiting my wife's relatives in D———, a town situated in one of those great states which adjoin Arkansas and the region pictured. Previous to this I had met nearly all my wife's people, and had liked them—as I still do. They were a pleasant, home-loving, if very conventional, company, all rather respected for their honesty, industry, and all those other admirable virtues which constitute in society its most sustaining and binding threads. Nearly all of them were well-to-do, interested in trade, banking, or farming, and all intensely interested in each other, at least to the extent of wishing to see that none fell below the ideals or standards of the group or class to which all belonged. As for ourselves, we were welcomed as peculiarly worthy examples of the social code they represented and the success for which they all strove.

"The region in which they lived was not unappea.-ing to me, even at first glance, although it was of that dead levelness that characterizes so much of the land west and east of the Mississippi. At longish intervals were those small grayish-white, humdrum, wooden towns, with their Main Street, their one or two church steeples, their few stores, and their straggly and not too often tree-shaded residence streets so characteristic of the then only partially formed America. The town, a part of which they were, numbered about fifteen hundred people, all of the same workaday, small-town type. The particular house which my wife's parents occupied was a simple, low, eight- or ten-room affair, standing at the extreme end of a street, the last house but one. (This other home, by the way, was occupied by another son-in-law, of some prominence in the local political world.) No pretense of show or luxury was here. The automobile had already arrived in some places, to be sure, but not here. In its stead were horses, buggies, wagons and the dreadful dirt roads that went with them. Cows, pigs, chickens, and geese were the usual equipment of all sturdy homes, even the most successful. To west and east and south stretched the level prairie with here and there a house, or a tree, or a barn, but mainly a flat, unobstructed, sun-baked world. Behold the fields! They were either deep and green with swaying, rustling corn, or faintly yellowing with wheat. Such trees as there were stood out ragged and lorn against a wealth of sky. A single-track railroad carried the trains of a great trunk line, but few of the trains stopped here. Farmers and strangers trailed in and out of town in buggies, wagons, or on horseback, always offering a genial 'Howdy?'

"I confess that in this seemly world—being an aspirant at letters, not trade—I at first felt a little out of place. Later, due to my real liking for these people, I felt much at home. Perhaps because I offered a sharp contrast to most of the other sons-in-law—being a writer, or 'artist,' maybe—a somewhat mysterious being, in short, who could afford, for some strange reason, to loaf or walk or sit before a desk at his ease and scribble upon paper with a pen—I was rather looked up to and made much of. Then, too, ordinarily I—week-day in and out—dressed in what here passed for Sunday and holiday best, whereas quite all these others—banker, grocer, politician, minister—wore during the week-days, at least, less carefully designed, albeit more picturesque and durable, garments. (And they possessed more material wealth than I at that time ever hoped to have!) So for weeks, or the length of our stay, there was a kind of holiday atmosphere among these same. We were different—hence interesting. Other sons and daughters, married and unmarried, came and went. They were a teasing, amusing lot, full of the silly quips and jests of the countryside and most loyal and affectionate where others of their group were concerned. And yet it was easy to see that their envies and rivalries underneath were in some cases very keen. They interested me as types, and I made common lot with them, giving and taking with their humors as best I might.

"My object during this holiday season was to write, and this I did when the holiday-making would permit. After a few days I was quite in love with the country —its broad, hot fields, the silent streets, the long, dusty roads, the farmers and the citizens and their simple, homely ways. Near at hand was a grave-yard, with a record of some sixty years of village life, and here I studied the tombstones. A mile or two away a creek trailed along between muddy, tree-shaded banks, and here I sat and fished. Over the way was the winter home of a well-to-do farmer and cattleman, a close neighbor of this family, which had been turned over to my parents-in-law for the summer. It was in this house, in a large, cool, and stiff 'parlor' such as most farmhouses boast, that I had my work-table and books and papers.

"However, in spite of a long procession of golden, sunshiny days, with bees that hummed, cows that tinkled distant bells, flower scents, bird calls and flashes, trains that whistled mournfully in the distance, I was unhappy. There was a void which no beauty of life, no social efforts to please or entertain, could quite fill. By day, by night, under the clear stars, I dreamed of love and beauty, and wished. For only see, see, life, the love-time, all beauty, was slipping away! My best years! And these people, however much I might like them, were still small-town souls, and would remain so. No fault of theirs. They could not think the thoughts I was thinking or gather the import of my dreams. The church, as I could see, meant everything to them spiritually. It eased the lacks of their lives in this world by promising them bliss in the next. Of books there were none, pictures none, music none, aspirations . . . well, here and there, perhaps an aspiring soul, but . . . In consequence, between reading Keats, Shelley, Hardy, Omar, and watching the procession of the days, I was by turns sad and gay. My wife, of course, offered me at least mental or spiritual companionship, but I was tired of her, preferring to be alone and work, or read, or walk and think.

"And then one day, to greet the new 'in-law' and to see what he was like, of course—came an additional brother-in-law, whom, as yet, I had not seen, that same aforementioned Howdershell, with wife and daughter, the latter a girl between seventeen and eighteen years of age and as pink and laughing and vivacious as one would wish to see. How truly simple and lovely youth can be at times—shapely, graceful, rhythmic, ruddy, with—in her case—a wealth of corn-colored hair, large, melting, gray-blue eyes, and small hands and feet. In short, on first glance and with a romantic and emotional ache because of my lorn state, I decided that she was exactly the type of physical loveliness of which I had been dreaming. Yet with no least knowledge of life or books, as any one could see; on the contrary, as she conveyed to me, at least—a gayety of spirit based on inexperience and illusion. Those innocent, non-coquettish smiles! That ringing laugh! That almost deranging sense of health in abundance! Those quick, easy, graceful movements! "Heavens!" I fairly gasped, "how utterly delicious and natural. For there was about her an innocent pertness, without a trace of brassy sophistication, that held me spellbound. Indeed, as I said to myself and at once, here was the natural geniality of one who knows all too little of life and assumes the world to be rather better than it is.

"But her father! That tall, lank, weather-indurated soul! Positively, he looked to have the tensile strength of whipcord and the ignorance of ten. He was lynx-eyed, self-opinionated, recessive, and suspicious, as becomes a United States marshal, I presume. Thus far in his career, as I now learned, he had captured one or two criminals of serious import, and, if I recall aright, had 'justifiably' slain two. Vain, courageous, opinionated, and yet reserved of speech, he stalked about in a long-tailed frock coat, his head adorned with one of those wide-brimmed sombreros so treasured of all American rurals—his hips carrying a pistol or two, I am sure. Yet, among relatives and friends he was the soul of geniality and, no doubt, clannish affection. Woe to any one who should chance to injure any of his, I thought, and worse, had a feeling that a Kentucky feudist would have done no more. His wife, as I have said, was small, talkative, cricket-like, and bounced here and there in a jumpy way. She was constantly relating anecdotes and incidents portraying the humors and eccentricities of her husband and others of this rural world. They lived, as I now learned, twenty-five miles to the south of this, in Arkansas and in a region of hills and picturesque river scenes, very different from this flat world in which we were.

"But it was this girl Rella who alone of all these now held my attention. Once having seen her I could scarcely turn my eyes from her as she moved here and there, running errands to the store or from one to another of her relatives, and finally, and gayly, setting the evening table for her grandmother. Truly, I thought, here is one who is startlingly beautiful. And so unusual —and so wholly uninformed. And yet the pull of her for me—the beauty, beauty, beauty of her! And to complete my enslavement, I was at once identified by her, and in the most innocent and affectionate of manners, as one of the family. For forthwith she addressed me as Uncle Dan, and apparently listed me among those most fortunate males of this family who were to be looked after by her and all of the women. Oh, what beauty, I thought! What eyes! What lips! What hair!

How trim and lissome a figure! Indeed, observing her now, I proceeded to meditate upon how two such homely persons as her parents could possibly have produced such a paragon!

"But, as always in those days, I decided forthwith that she was not for me, and prepared in a dreary way to make the best of it. Incidentally, I was conscious of the eyes of my wife, watchful and jealous. No least show of interest on my part, however innocent, could escape her, as I knew, and it would at once be interpreted as evidence of potential, if not plotted, unfaithfulness. Her manner at such times was most disturbing to me, and fiercely and instantly now I resented this espionage. To be sure, from her point of view she was right, or at least within her rights, in trying to defend her interests or forfend against a destructive affection of any kind. But what about myself? My dreams? And to preserve this present and only seeming stability of our relationship required a great deal more than watchfulness, I thought—a reflection which made me sad. That love should fade! That one's happiness should end! Any one's! And only love, as I knew, could preserve one's dreams. Not self-interest. I registered a sorrowful, and yet useless, sympathy for her. For of what value is sympathy to one who has no power to compel a real affection?

"The first night passed, and by morning I was doubly conscious of an irritated mood in regard to all this—my marriage, my contracted and controlled actions, and, so, life itself. God! To be cribbed, cabined, confined! Why had I so early in life handicapped myself in the race for happiness? What a fool, to tie myself down in this way! Would I never be free again? Here was this laughing, happy, beautiful creature who but for this early mistake might now be mine. But . . . was I sure of that? Could she be made to care for me? No, no, no! Married or unmarried, how should I . . . being as unattractive as I was . . . attract her? Nevertheless, it was some satisfaction to me to find that after the first day she was still here. She had not flown, and love or no love, I would still have the delight of looking at her. And to my intense delight, on the second day I discovered that they were to remain a week.

"Yet that very morning, just the same, I went sorrowfully to my desk, thinking that it were best, perhaps, if I were to shut myself away from all this. I could not ever have her, anyhow—so why brood? Yet that afternoon, idling because idleness seemed in the air, I sat in a hammock and watched this girl and her cousin, the daughter of the politician over the way, race about, mock quarreling over the possession of a trinket. Later, because of a friendly laugh from me, they came to the hammock and sat with me, each taking an arm and proceeding to examine the book I had been reading. But this proving of no interest, they soon turned to the playful labor of swinging me in spite of a pretended wish on my part not to be swung. But by this time the mere proximity of this girl was proving toxic. I was made faint, as well as hungry, by the fullness of her beauty. A feeling of languor alternated with one of intense depression over the brevity of so great a joy as well as the inadequacy of any act or qualification of mine to interest such beauty, youth, innocence. A deadly drug could not have acted with greater power. In vain I told myself that if by so much as a look I should betray even a trace of what I was feeling I would be thereafter most carefully avoided, not only by herself but by her relatives. . . . In vain! I could not help yearning over her. And how intensely. And yet, also—for the nonce, at least—I played the tolerant young uncle, fourteen years her senior and very circumspect and emotionally if not amusedly unconcerned. She was not for me! Not for me. And then, heartsick because of the seeming remoteness of this youthful world which never again could know me as a citizen, I was ready to give over and return to my writing room over the way.

"Yet now—miracle of miracles!—it seemed to me that she was more than ordinarily playful, springing into the hammock with me and once there attempting to push me out or upset me. And the feel of her arms, body—her glorious young strength tugging at me! And later she took my book from me and began to read in a mock solemn voice, her pretty head pushed close to mine. But when of a sudden, as I also noted, she saw my wife approaching, she straightened and assumed a more distant air. Now, thought I, what does that mean?

"That same afternoon I, having gone back to my desk and returned, one of my cousins-in-law volunteering to root plantain weeds out of the lawn with a dibble, I joined her, working with a table knife and fork for want of anything better. And the day being so fine, my thoughts soon wandered off to her whom above all earthly things I now so suddenly craved. How magical now the sunlight on the grass—the shade of the trees in the sunlight and this simple dooryard and lawn! Had I not seen her tripping over it but an hour before? Four trees spaced evenly beyond the street walk threw a grateful shade. If one could sit here with her! But the hammock was now occupied by the marshal, who proceeded to make sport of us workers.

" 'Better come down to my farm,' he jibed. 'We've got lots nicer weeds down there.'

" 'Let's see the weeds!' I called, hopefully.

" 'Dare you to come down and even look at 'em,' he returned, mockingly.

"I was tempted to accept, but just then the paragon herself appeared, returning from the village post office with letters. And quickly, laughing over the great work, finding a fork and joining us. She had donned a slate-blue apron, which caused her yellow hair to take on an added luster. Seating herself nearby, she too dug and jested.

" 'Oh, here's one with a whopper of a root! I'm afraid I'll never be able to get this one out without help!'

Needless to say, I went to her aid.

"And then, because of her gay spirits, I had an intense longing to play with her. To further this desire I suggested a game of mumblety-peg, and she agreed, asserting at the same time that she could beat me or anyone any day. A pocket knife was produced, and we sat on the grass facing each other. Her gestures seemed to take on an innocent artfulness. She cocked her head, parted her lips in an interested and expectant manner before each throw, and pouted so demurely when she failed. I could scarcely play for watching her. The wisps of damp hair about her forehead! The mock intenseness of her eyes! The sweet rhythmic value of her gestures! Once, as she was holding the knife to her chin preparatory to tossing it, she looked straight into my eyes. My senses reeled. That dreamy, tremulous glance—that faraway something that was like an inner sea of blue dotted with romancing sails—what could it mean? Then she spoke softly, almost in a whisper: 'I'll miss if you look at me like that.'

" 'Miss, then.'

"I continued to gaze, confused by her brazen coquetry and my limitations in the field of gallantry and courage and charm. Another relative, unconscious of this tête à tête, joining us, we made it a three and later a four-handed game. Soon after I retired to brood over the meaning of her words and the splendor of her beauty. For hours I could do nothing but sit and dream of her, confused and all but numb with joy. I could not, and would not, believe that she was becoming interested in me. That could not be. And yet . . . that playful and yet seeking look; that excited and enticing laugh when we were alone. I went to my desk in the house across the street, dubious of the import of it all and yet tremulously elate. Just before six, to my immense surprise and delight she came, bearing a bowl of nasturtiums and a pitcher of water, which she handed through the window before my desk.

" 'Aunt V—— said I might bring these,' and with this came a warm friendly glance. And: 'You must begin to get ready for dinner now. I'm making biscuit. Do you like biscuit?'

" 'If you're making them, I'll like them,' I said, moved beyond the meaning of my words by her charm and the joyous manner in which she did everything. 'But how well you do your hair!' I added, for want of another thought.

" 'Oh, if you tell me things like that, I'll make you lots of nice things!'

" 'You are all the nice things. You needn't make me anything. May I tell you that?' I looked at her pleadingly.

"She began to move away, but without any suggestion of fear or reproach—rather as though it were quite all right, only not best for her to answer. I sensed her wisdom and said no more. But as she crossed the yellow, dusty road, still warm though the cool of the evening was at hand, I studied her. Her figure suggested that of one who might dance divinely. I was beside myself with delight. Could it really be that there was springing up between myself and this girl, my aged self and this bud, an understanding which, were I but free, could profit me so gloriously?

"But as I was thinking, my wife came to fetch me, and behold—weariness of soul! What could be the end of this? How could there be anything other than a hopeless, fruitless infatuation, ending in negation and enforced regulation? None the less, I was caught in the grip of an affection that was tumbling me pellmell whithersoever it would. And all about me the warmth of this wonderful summer—a land bucolic and fecund. That great red ball in the west that was only now sinking beneath the level of the grass there. And this air, heavy with odors, floral and moving. The lowing of cattle only a little distance away. The twittering evensong of birds. The spreading shadows, soon to be begemmed with stars . . . I stood in a side door facing the west and sighed over my lot, viewing this painter's dream before me.

"The next morning, on pretext of bringing me a pitcher of water and more flowers—(services which I could not understand my wife permitting)—Rella came inside the room where I worked. She stood beside my chair and looked over my shoulder at a half-written page.

" 'Oh, what a small straight hand! You almost write backwards, don't you? You ought to see my scrawl!' She was leaning over me, her face near mine—her cheek. And giggling infectiously. She affected me like fire.

" 'No flattery, now!' I half choked. 'I write badly, and I know it. But let me see how you do. I'll bet you write beautifully.'

" 'Oh, gee!' (A gurgle.) 'I used to get such scoldings at school. Once my teacher hit me over the knuckles with her ruler. And she always said my I's looked like J's. See!'

" 'They look like stars now,' I said. I was looking into them as I said this. More, I had placed an arm about her and was holding her, which caused her to flush and exclaim, 'Oh!' All at once I drew her to me, bringing her yellow hair close to my mouth. I put a hand to her chin and pulled her face close to mine. There was color in her cheeks, a weak, yielding look in her eyes. Our lips met. Suddenly she straightened up.

" 'I'd better be going now,' she said, a little flustered.

" 'No, I have you now.'

" 'I must! I can't stay.'

"She permitted me to kiss her again. Her lips flamed against mine. I let her go and she ran out, stopping to lean over a bed of nasturtiums in order to recover herself. I sat and meditated. Could only a dreary separation be the end of this? For three days more we met in hallways and corners, among flower-bushes and trees, and in the old house across the way when an errand could be contrived. Once she said: 'Would you like me to come to New York when I've finished school?'

" 'Would I!' was all I could say. She danced away, adding as she went: 'Maybe I will, if I can.' A wild dream anent the possibilities of this filled my mind for days.

"By some irony of chance at this time, her father now began to display a sudden and affectionate interest in me. He began to linger in my presence, discussing the area in which he was an officer, the politics and social friendships and biases which governed the execution of his orders. Like so many others at that time, he was curious as to the charm of New York and desirous of visiting there. Agreeably I asked him to visit us, and thereafter nothing would do but that we must visit him at his ranch, some twenty-five miles distant. He would rig up a working chamber for me in the house or the barn. If I liked, I could work in an old sheep-shearer's hut on a hill not far from the house, and one of the children could see that I was called in time for dinner, or would bring it to me there. (Rella, said my mind.) More, we could return with them now. Later he would send one of his sons over for our trunks. I might stay the winter and see the character of life in the Ozarks.

"Where but an hour before I was facing pitch gloom at the thought of certain and impending separation, I was now at once beside myself with happy anticipation. But, in order to misdirect suspicion, I pretended to doubt the wisdom of imposing upon such liberality. It was too kind of him. It could not be. I really could not. But this merely sharpened his insistence, as I hoped it would. And to make doubly sure that I should be swayed, he set about coaxing my wife, who, to my surprise and delight, was rather in favor of the journey. So, she had noticed nothing, I decided. And at last and to my sardonic pleasure it was she who persuaded me to go.

"At dusk then one evening a day or two later, we set forth to drive the twenty-five miles. It has been a number of years now, but to this hour I can scent the odor of grasses and blooms and vines and bushes, wet with the dews of night. Through rocky valleys and along clear streams, which rippled and murmured over pebbly beds, the light three-seated vehicle, drawn by two spirited mares, rolled and careened. On either hand immense fields of corn and wheat and hay new-mown glinted dimly and spectrally under a full moon. Here and there bats and owls winged their lumbering ways, and beetles in full flight bumbled and thumped against us. In distant cottages winked yellow lights, and overhead was the bright moon, all but blotting out the stars. Because Mrs. Howdershell wished to talk about New York and my work there, I was squeezed in between her and Rella. I recall my joy now when a furtive little hand was laid in mine under the blanket. The exchange of glances in the moonlight! Her gay laughter and comments! The shine of the moonlight in her eyes!

"Life at moments verges upon sheer magic. The astonishing impulse to generation and decay which we call living so richly orchestrates itself at times, so sensitively responds to exterior tones, odors, shadows, as to achieve witchery. The blending is so moving. So profoundly we dream; so eagerly we seek.

"It seemed to me, as we rode at first between level fields, then over low hills, and through dreamy, misty valleys, that life, try as it might, could never attain anything more wonderful than this. Indeed, so intense was my mood, so great was the pull between myself and this girl, that I was all but translated to a less tangible realm, where life seemed to be dream rather than a reality. And yet, sadly, too—oh, how sadly and mournfully—I speculated as to whether anything permanent could come of this. How might I seize her? How, in all her bright beauty, keep her? Strangely, and without immediate cause, I was jealous of every one—her parents and the future. Should I win her, or might not some other take her from me? The bitterness of that! I was riddled with pain by speculations as to loss, not victory. My wife! My wife! Married, married! The words were as the notes of a tolled bell. And yet, in truth, I was not interested (even in her case), in a long-enduring marriage or the usual formal procedures in relation to love. Had I not secured this girl who was my wife, and did I now desire her permanently? But why not? Darkly I speculated as to why love should necessarily pass into this more formalistic and irksome relationship, only later to end in death. I questioned, (and reasonably enough, I think), whether all women wished to be married permanently. It seemed to me that many—the more beautiful ones, at least—scorned marriage. Yet I personally was at a loss as to how to provide a saner method of procedure. Tragedy or dissatisfaction or ennui seemed to lurk at every corner and down every path; danger, death, and extremes of all kinds to provide the very necessary fillip whereby love found its zest and continuance.

"At the same time, the attitude of this girl puzzled me. For her parents, strict and dogmatic people both, had, no doubt, emphasized to her all the social virtues as they understood them. And yet here she was now, playing at love with one whom she knew to be married. My wife, her aunt, before her in the seat beside Howdershell—and so jealous and suspicious, as Rella already sensed I was sure. But did that in any way affect her? It did not. Could youth, strongly shaken by life's primal and driving impulse, be so affected? I knew well it could not. All the solemn lessons inculcated thus far were plainly as nothing to her. She too was in love. The misery which might ensue to her aunt counted as nothing. She either could not understand or would not consider.

"As the night wore on we finally descended into a valley surrounded by great hills. Through this valley ran a stream, its waters tumbling over white stones, and sparkling and rippling in the moonlight. A single light far to the right was hailed as home. And, as we drew nearer, I made out a great barn near the stream. And then came the house, shadowed by several great trees. I helped Rella and her mother down and followed them toward the house, where, as we neared it, we met two young, strong, sleepy sons coming to greet us.

" 'I'll tell you what you do, Rella,' called the mother, enthusiastically. 'Take a candle and go down to the cellar and bring up some apples and cider.'

"Forthwith I was invited to carry the candle and a basket, while she carried the pitcher. Lighted by one feeble, yellow flame, we kissed in the shadows under the beamed floor, and then gathered a few apples and drew a pitcher of amber juice. I recall the thrill and bubble of Rella's manner, the magic of her young face vaguely illuminated, the sense of danger in her eyes.

" 'You'd better let me go now. Aunt V—— might come down.'

"Thinly experienced in life and its vagaries at the time, I was full of wonder that one so young and seemingly inexperienced could so practically and tactfully relinquish what she so obviously desired in favor of what might later be. Yet events were to demonstrate to me that caution, a sense of balance and self-protection, were as much a part of Rella's make-up as her gayety and affection. Only no undue emphasis was placed on caution; as a matter of fact, she seemed to me unconscious of danger; and yet the quickness with which she was ready to seize a favorable opportunity, or to relinquish a dangerous moment, showed all too clearly how innate and secure was her sense of intrigue and the fitness or unfitness of the deeds and moments that compounded it. After one such moment as this, she could return—as I now saw—to the others, and with the air of one whom love has never touched.

"(Bright bird! Beautiful butterfly! Let me hold you, your wings untarnished!)

"The cider, cookies and apples disposed of, all confessed to weariness, and retired, while I once more wandered forth into the night. It was all too beautiful and exciting, and I could not sleep. Instead I walked, sitting finally upon the slope of one of the hills that rose directly behind the house, and meditating under the stars. Oh, love, love, I thought! Youth, youth! The fever, the agony of this infection! How could it have flown so quickly in the one case only to burst so quickly into flame in another? Were we, after all, but vials of fluid, compounded by another than ourselves and reacting to laws or stimuli which had little or nothing in common with our own social theories and procedures? Or it seemed so—as though the very electrons of one's being in conclave assembled, or as by revolution voted or decided or swayed one, and that in the face of the staid polity of the world without. But whatever it was, the fever was exquisite. I burned. I ached. God, I thought, her exquisite young face, her graceful young body, her motions, smile, eyes. That they should do this to me . . . and to her, maybe! Or could it, in her case? Was it so doing? Did she really love me—respond as I was responding? The thought was so painful that I could not longer endure it and so arose and returned to the silent house.

"But the next morning I was up early, eager to see her first. The slightest glimpse of her was fire. And beside this delicious country land in July time, its smooth, green hills, its wide yellowing fields of wheat, and the still green fields of corn. The stream, an adjacent wood, a white ribbon of road leading out in two directions, all interested me. Within the barnyard were pigs and chickens, and about the eaves of the barn strutted a flock of pigeons. A cultivated field of vines, heavy with raspberries and still half-grown blackberries, adjoined the house lot. In the fields beyond the men were already reaping, my host and his sons among them.

"After an hour or two spent in idling about, I returned to the house, to find upon a shaded kitchen veranda commanding a wide panorama, a table spread with berries and cream, coffee, bacon and eggs, and fresh biscuit, as well as milk and buttermilk—and all offered with apologies! My wife, wishing to help her sister, had already eaten, thus leaving me to make the best of a meal supervised by Rella. Yet I could scarcely eat for looking into her fresh young face—her eyes, her mouth, her hair!

"At the same time I was writing for several magazines, but I found myself scarcely able to work for thinking of her—the hope of seeing her, hearing her voice, looking into her eyes, touching her hand, all but deranging me mentally. And to increase the fever, she was here and there throughout the day, laughing, encountering me, at times, seemingly on purpose, at others avoiding me. There were calves and chickens to feed, a cake to make, furniture to dust. Gayly, as one who makes a pleasure of such tasks, she went about them, smiling or singing as she worked. Once, her hair down about her shoulders, she waved to me from an upper window. Another time she came to me where I wrote, presumably to bring water, but really for a kiss —yet how slyly, and with a cautioning finger to her lips.

"Beyond the barn was a great corn field—a huge lake of corn—and beyond this the hut of an old fisher and trapper, who had come to the house on our first day and in whose life I had expressed a keen interest; thereby winning an invitation to call. When I spoke of going to visit him, I was told by Rella how easily I might go by a path which followed a fence and then cut through the field. 'And if you come back along the eighth row,' she whispered, 'I might meet you.'

"At any other time I would have found this man interesting. In his hut were silver and red fox skins from this very region. He knew the art of fishing and hunting and had traveled as far west as the coast of California. But all the afternoon my heart and mind were elsewhere. I wanted the sun to sink, the evening perfumes to rise, to meet Rella among the rustling corn.

"And at last I took my leave, eager—feverish, even— and yet dawdling along the path between rows of corn that whispered and chaffered of life, and myself reciting scraps of a dozen poems. The perfume of the ground, the wind among the stalks and the distant trees, the calls of the birds—how they tortured now with their sweetness! Indeed, they thrilled and fevered me as might great verse, having the lilt and ring of great lines. Of a sudden life seemed young, unbelievably glorious. For I saw her afar tripping between the sworded corn, her head bare, an apron holding something and yet tied so as to take care of itself. She looked behind her from time to time as she came, and then drew near and put up her arms. I held her close and poured into her ear the fascination she exercised for me. She did not speak at first, merely holding her lips to mine, then prattled of the weariness of the day without me. But soon she declared, as always: 'But I can't stay. I must run. They think I'm in the barn.' She left me, and misery settled upon me again.

"There was another day. I went to a small stream to

fish, hoping that she would visit me there. And where I stopped, vines and overhanging branches contrived a dell in which was a pool, a sandy beach, and fish visible in the clear water. Arcady. Wondering where she was and what she was doing, I turned, and there she was, peeping out from behind some greenery a dozen yards away. Dinner was only an hour off and yet she had brought me cake and a glass of milk in a small basket. 'I suggested it to Aunt V——,' she laughed, 'and she told me to bring them.' She laughed again. I took her in my arms.

"The ground beneath the trees was mottled with sunshine. The small strand was of golden sand, as yellow as her hair. Beyond the stream was a solid, lichen-covered wall of gray granite, rising all of thirty feet, and behind us a thicket of bushes, making of this leafy place an almost secret chamber. Alone with her here I felt freest of all, yet always in danger. For could we know whether we had been or were being observed? Howdershell, her mother, brothers, my wife. And yet, regardless, I ventured to hold her here, and she to submit, pulling her to a stone and sealing her mouth with mine. At last she ran away, picking up her basket as she went. Fifty feet away she put her head through some leaves and smiled back at me. 'You're not catching many fish, are you?' And she was gone.

"The next morning, before sunrise, I was up and out, seeking some dewberries I had seen growing near the wall of wood at the south end of the berry field.

The wood-perfumed air and wet grass underfoot gave me a sense of living, breathing poetry, of life dreamily and beautifully lived. A surging sense of the newness and perpetual youth of the world was upon me. Here, I said, in the face of all individual age and death, in such fevers as these, in such moments as these, life contemptuously shows how forever young and new it is. I may age, or another. I may die, or another. But life and youth go on. Sunrises come and go, and they are new to those who are newly come. The birds also, and the trees. New springs, new summers, new autumns, new winters, new springs again. New blood is being created to continue the whole thing forever. But what of my love? What of my unhappy marriage? Soon this must end. I must end. And then what? How much, if any, of this eternal newness for me?

"And, as though to punish me for my gloomy philosophy, from that day on things seemed to take a turn for the worse. I had expected Rella to follow me into this glorious dawn to pick berries with me, but she did not. Instead, as she told me later, she could not—her mother had remarked that she might be annoying me. Later in the day I told her I was going to the stream to fish, but she did not come. Her mother had filled her moments with tasks. So that day passed, and with glances only, and those darkly veiled. The next day was almost as bad. I was beginning to feel that the shadow of suspicion was darkening this scene and making my stay untenable. Yet late that afternoon, having been for a walk and coming down the hill at the back of the house, I found her picking berries. She had on an old sunbonnet of her mother's, and looked the fresh and innocent schoolgirl that she was, a fit companion for the summer and the fields. I felt sick at the thought of losing her.

" 'Want to help me?' she began, with a safeguarding glance in the direction of the house.

" 'Oh, do I?' I replied, drawing near.

" 'But I don't know,' she began at once. 'I believe mamma suspects. You'd better not stand so close,' and she pointed to a bush a few feet away.

" 'Rella,' I said, bending over the more distant bush and yet talking to her, 'you don't know—I can't tell you how it is with me. I want you so. I can scarcely sleep. What will come of this, do you suppose? Could you come to New York ever? Would you run away with me if I wanted you to?'

" 'Oh,' she paused meditatively. 'I don't know. I hadn't thought of that, you know. I don't think I could now—not yet, anyhow—but I might come sometime if Aunt V—— would let me.' She looked at me earnestly, dubiously, then laughed amusedly at this last thought.

"I felt a sinking sensation at the pit of my stomach. This optimism. This laughter here and now. Could she really feel as I felt—sense any of my great want? I feared not—almost *knew* not—and my heart was

heavy, my spirit prone on the earth. I stared helplessly.

" 'I don't know how I'm going to get along without
you, Rella,' I sighed.

" 'Oh, I'll miss you terribly, too,' she said, but not as
I had said what I had said. It was all too tragic to me.

" 'Oh, Rella!' I went on, feverishly. 'Do you really
love me?'

" 'Yes.' She bent over the bush.

" 'Do you?'

" 'Yes. Yes. But you'd better look out, Uncle Dan.
They might see you from the house.'

"I moved away. 'How can I go away and leave you?'

" 'Oh, how I wish I could go with you! I do! I do!'
was all she said. We talked but little more then, for
her mother called to her for something.

"The next afternoon, working in the shade of an east
porch which ran along the side of the house, I was
made well aware that Rella was making as much of
my presence as conditions would permit. She passed
almost too often for one alive to the need of distracting
attention, and finally, in order to be near me, as I
guessed, decided to wash her hair so that she might
come out and sun it near me, and perhaps
—the vanity and coquetry of girlhood!—parade
its golden glory to my view. Only, as she
said,—whispering it to me at first—she could not
stay long. The atmosphere of suspicion in connection
with us was plainly too great. But she could, and did,

manage to pass and repass on one errand and another between the sunny veranda where I was and the inner room in which she was, touching me each time with either her hand or her skirt. And the glory of her bright hair now loose, haloing her wonderfully vivid and youthful face—the water-clarity of her eyes—the exquisite form and fullness of her lips! How mad it was, I said to myself over and over now, for me to even look at her, let alone wish. For was not, as I now noticed for the first time, my wife observing us from a window? Yet Rella again, passing me, stopped and asked me to *feel* her hair, how soft and fine it was. And as she did so the look she bent on me was one of sick repression—a look which greatly reassured me as to her own feeling for me, at the same time that it reduced me the more because of the immanence of loss. To think of her eyes speaking this longing! In spite of my wife, who was not visible at the moment, I took the mass of it in my hands and pulled her face toward me. She looked swiftly about, then gave me an eager, swift kiss, and went on. Scarcely had she done so though than my wife appeared in the doorway. There was in her eyes, as I saw at once, a hard, brilliant light which showed only when she was very angry. She went into the house again, only to return and just as Rella had ventured to come out once more. And now she said: 'Rella! Your mother wants you.'

"From that moment I realized that the worst impended. Black looks and secret persistent spying were

in store for me. And a series of veiled, if not open,
comments. For she would not, as I now knew, stay
here any longer. And without her, how could I? What
excuse would there be? Sadly, if dourly, I proceeded to
face realities. Apart from going with her if she decided
now to go, there was but one thing—and that radical
and incautious—an elopement with Rella. But, sup-
posing the plan were put to her, would she say yes?
If not, then what? Defeat and misery, of course. And
yet, should she consent . . . then what? The hard and
savage Howdershell, once he knew; the whispered and
open comments in this region. Rella's repute. Mine.
The vengeful ire of my loving but jealous wife. For
needless to say, one such move on my part and she
would seek redress of Howdershell himself; effect, if
possible, the return of Rella at any cost. And as for
myself, once away with Rella, then what? The battle;
the pursuit; the expense and social and mental dis-
ruption of flight. I was ensnared, yes—and oh, how
much! The agony of it! But this . . . to Rella . . .
to me . . . to all. Slowly, but surely, sadly and grimly
—being neither radical nor incautious—I faced the
inevitable.

"And from that hour, as I feared, I was met
with suggestions from my wife as to the un-
wisdom of a longer visit here. A message from
the home of her parents,—or so she said—had
already urged us to return there—for some event
of no importance—a street fair, I think. Also

the valuelessness of a longer stay in the west was emphasized. Was I not becoming weary of this country life? But when I pretended not to understand the meaning of this sudden change from pleasure in all this to a desire to leave, there were at first looks, then a fit of dark depression, and finally tears. I knew what was wrong. Did I dare pretend that I did not? I . . . I . . . who had done this . . . that . . . And so, in a flood, a flashing picture of my evil heart. Ah, what was I not? Had I no shame, no decency? Were innocent young school girls not safe even in their own homes? Was I not astounded at myself, my scandalous temerity in attempting a flirtation with a girl fourteen years my junior, a mere girl in her teens, and who, by the way, ought to be ashamed of herself, too? It was high time we were getting out of here. We would go, and we would go at once—now—to-morrow!

"But, no—we would not go to-morrow—we wouldn't go before the following Monday, if then—and it was I who said so! Let her rage! Let her tell the family, but I would not go unless ordered by them, if she wished that. I was resting. Why should I leave? To avoid a possibly trying scene for herself, she finally yielded to this. But with stormy words and in a tempestuous mood. And so it was, with this situation in mind, that I was now compelled to face Rella—to tell her softly and with suggestions as to caution for herself, how matters stood. It was she who was being blamed, as well as myself—she, as well as myself, who had a problem to face—the first and greatest she had ever faced—and a dangerous one for her as well as myself. And now, how would she do? Elope with me, for instance, or stay here and lose me? And how did she feel? Was she at all frightened? Could she, and would she, think and act for herself?

"But now, to my surprise and satisfaction, instead of exhibiting any trace of fear or tremulousness, she merely faced me, cool, even pale. It was too bad, wasn't it? Dreadful. If only she were a little older. She had hoped we would not be found out, but since we had been . . . perhaps . . . perhaps . . . well . . . Perhaps the best thing was to wait. And her father and mother might cause trouble right now because of Aunt V——, and what she might do. But later . . . listen . . . next winter she would be going to school over at Fayetteville, a hundred miles away. How about coming over there? We could see each other there. The fifteen hundred miles that would lie between us at that time were, as it seemed to me then, all but meaningless to her. I could do anything, very likely. And yet, I knew so well that I could not—that she did not understand. I was poor, not rich; married, not free; shackled by the forces of life as much as she was, if not more, and yet dreaming of freedom and love, wishing to fly.

"And so it was that late that night, walking up the hill that lay to the south of the house, I was a prey to the gloomiest of thoughts. Despite a certain respect for convention and order which was still strong within me, the rude and haphazard compulsion which I now saw operative in all nature about me suggested another and less orderly course. For was I to be thrown to and fro like a ball by this intense desire; derive no reward? No, no, no! Never, never, never! For this girl cared for me, and if pleaded with would yield, would she not? From where I sat even now I could see a light in Rella's room, and if I were to whistle or signal in some way, I knew she would come. But on the other hand, there was this respect—to a degree at least—for the feelings of these, her parents. And not only that but the fear of consequences to Rella and myself. Did she really know her own mind as yet? Could she? Was she really, truly, in love? Ah . . . the light in that window! Her unloosened hair . . . her face! I meditated a further extension of time here . . . beyond Monday . . . beyond the following week, even. But there was the battle that would have to be fought between myself and my wife. And betimes could she not, and would she not, whisper to her sister, the mother of this girl? And then what? The departure of Rella, of course.

"Beyond where I sat, the light poured like filtered silver over the fields of corn and wheat, and the patches of meadow bordered by squares of dark wood. Here and there in a small house still winked a yellow lamp. Dogs barked, hounds bayed, an owl or two 'woohooed'. And yet, for upwards of an hour, I sat thus, my head in my hands, meditating on beauty, and love,

and change, and death. Life was too bitter and too
sweet, I sighed, begrudging every fleeting moment of it
here. For soon, in spite of all I might do now, this
visit would be over. And I would return to D——, and
then to New York. And when, if ever again, would I
see Rella? When? Her tall, cold, thin-minded father,
how I wearied of him now! And her mother, what of
her? Could, or would, Rella ever really wish to escape
the corded meshes of their goodness, their virtues? So,
brooding, I sighed, and in heaviness of soul finally
arose and started down the hill. Yet, halfway down, in
the shadow of the wood alongside which ran the path,
I was startled by a hooded figure hurrying toward me.
Nearing me, the shawl was thrown back, the head
lifted, and,—it was Rella, perfect but pale in the sheen
of the moon!

" 'Darling!' I exclaimed.

" 'I had to come,' she gasped. 'I couldn't stay away
any longer. I know it's late, but I slipped out. I hope no
one heard. I was afraid I might not get to talk to you
again. Mother suspects, I think. And Aunt V—— has
talked to her. But I had to come! I had to!' She was
short of breath from running.

" 'But, honey, dearest! Your mother! Your father! If
they should see you!'

"I paused, for I was thinking of something else now.
For here she was with me at last, had come of her own
accord. Therefore, now . . . since . . . was I not justified in . . . ? I paused, holding her, a strong, pos-

sessive, almost ruthless, fever driving me. And yet, so philosophic and reflective was my mind that even now I could not help asking myself in what unsophistication, unworldly innocence, was it that she had really come here—one too young, truly, to know the full import of her own actions or desires. But holding close to me and babbling of her love.

"'I know papa's over at Walter's, and mamma's in bed. So is Aunt V——. I went up to my room and then slipped down. They won't know. I sometimes come out this way. But I had to see you! I had to! But, oh, I can't stay! You know I can't! It would be terrible for you if I were seen here. You don't know my father.'

"'I know, I know, dear,' I whispered. 'You little innocent, you sweetheart,' and I drew her head against my shoulder and kissed her and smoothed her hair. 'But how did you know I was here, and how shall I do without you now? Will you be mine? Will you go with me now—to-morrow—next day?'

"She looked up at me nervously and seemingly comprehendingly, thoughts of many things apparently scampering through her mind, then hid her face in my coat.

"'Oh, no, no, not now!' she said. 'I can't. I know . . . I know what you mean . . . but I can't. Not this way. Not now. You don't know my father, or my mother, either. He would kill you. Yes, he would. Oh, dear! I mustn't stay. I mustn't. I knew you were going, and I had to come. I couldn't stay away. Maybe next winter . . . if you would come for me. . . .' And she drew nervously away.

" 'Yes,' I replied, wearily, sensing the impossibility of it all. And thinking: If Howdershell should know—if he should even guess! And yet you coming this way, just when I want you most—when it is hardest to resist. And not even understanding clearly. God! And in a storm of pain I held her, saying: 'Next winter, maybe, if I can arrange it. So go now. And write me. I will slip you an address to-morrow. And I will write you here, or anywhere, anywhere you say!'

" 'Oh, yes, yes, at Fayetteville. That's sure, is it?' she gasped, hurriedly. 'But I must go. I'll write you, sure.'

"She hurried down the hill in the shadow, and I gazed after her. The end—the end—I thought. There was blood on the thought. I heard a collie bark, then saw the kitchen door open and some one look out. I could only hope that she had safely reached her room.

"Coming out by the woodpile below the house some ten minutes later I stood gazing at the scene which the house presented. It was so simple, so rural—a strong, beamed affair, with rambling rooms, angles, small verandas and windows. But now no light. And inside Rella, safe, I hoped, not having been seen. But thinking what, now that she was alone? As I was? Or was she? But I loving her so. And beaten! Beaten by circumstances,—life, parents, marriage, I know not what. I cursed, and hated, even, for I was sick of love—poisoned by it, even.

"And then, of a sudden, as I stood there—and from nowhere, as it were, out of the dark or mist but without a sound—directly before me Howdershell! And cool and still in the moonlight, not a word issuing from his lips, his steady, green-blue eyes fixed upon me. Aha, I thought! Trapped! He has seen, heard! Now then, what? The worst, I suppose. The storm. I braced myself, my blood chilling. I was unarmed and I knew he was always armed.

"'A fine night, isn't it?' he began, calmly and, as I thought, coldly pretending a friendship he did not feel. (The instinct of the trapper, I added to myself. It is so he begins. How should I have hoped to defeat him?) My veins were running ice water. 'Been out for a walk?' His words had, to me, a mocking sound.

"'Yes,' I replied, as calmly as I could.

"To my immense relief, almost my amazement, he now began drawling concerning a horse that had been, and still was, sick, and that had needed his attention. Also of a neighbor who had come to assist him with his wheat. And damp with perspiration, I listened, concluding after a time that after all he had seen nothing, suspected nothing. Then this secret approach was without significance, a country gesture, the sly quip of one who liked to surprise and frighten another? But with what consequences, really, had he come upon Rella and myself!

"And then Monday—the day set by my wife for our departure but with us staying over for a day or two just the same. Yet, because of this shock—the dubious mood evoked in me by this moonlight meeting—no further attempt on my part to persuade Rella against her will. Rather only a dark, oppressive realization of the futility of all this. Yet, love and desire, an enthralling and devastating sense of her beauty—of what union, even free companionship, with her must mean. And so the pain of restraint and loss.

"Deep amid the tall, whispering corn, only one day before I left, a last meeting with her, to say good-bye. And it was she who, watchful, elusive, contrived it. She would write . . . she would come, even. I need not fear. And then, kisses, kisses. And after that, what glances! And almost before the eyes of her parents and her aunt. The lovelight that beckoned! At breakfast on that last morning she even sighed as she handed me something. I was wondering if she was really feeling as I was.

" 'Don't you want me to send her poisoned candy?' she whispered, jestingly. This was apropos of a celebrated poisoning case then in the papers.

" 'Rella!' I reproved. The thought startled me.

" 'Oh, I wouldn't, but I feel like it,' she said, sadly.

"The stark, merciless, unheeding nature of love was being brought home to me then with a greater force than ever before. For here was youth, innocence, beauty —a paragon in form, really—and yet what was the defeat of this other woman to her? Nothing. A blood relation, and yet an enemy to be defeated. And as for life and law? What were they to this eager, seeking girl? Either not understood or only dimly, perhaps, and scoffed at. Yet even I in my fever could not help thinking of the ruthlessness of life. And yet, such was my own infatuation that now in nowise could I be displeased with her for her fierce thought. Rather I was inflamed by it—made more desirous—perceiving as I did through this the depths of nature in this girl.

"And then, at parting, to see her boldly and proudly put her lips to mine (and that in the very face of her aunt), and then turn and offer those same lips to her, which offer was icily accepted. And all this before her mother, (who must have known, yet for diplomatic reasons did not wish to indicate her knowledge), and her father, and the other members of the family. Even now I recall my wife's eyes, clouded with hate and suppressed rage. And Rella smiling and defiant, proud in her young beauty. And then myself, riding back over the hills and through the valleys to D——, and despite the mood of the woman beside me, lost in reflections that were immensely depressing—to her as well as to myself.

For here I was, for all my fever and tossing, defeated. And my wife, for all her defeat, still, after a fashion, victorious. Yet both unhappy. And Rella, too. And so, further reflections as to the essential helplessness, and even slavery, of man—and this despite all his formulæ and in the face of his compelling passions. And so sickening because of the anachronisms of life. For here was I, wishing most intensely to be doing one thing and yet being shunted along this wretched path of custom and duty against my will. And afraid, or unable, to break the chains which held me. And behind me, Rella, who for all her strong desire and daring, was helpless. And beside me a woman, fuming and brooding about a force she could not possibly control, yet resolved never to resign what was 'rightfully' hers, and so clinging to the ashes of a long-since burnt-out love. And the parents of Rella and my wife's parents assuming that happiness and order reigned where instead was molten and explosive opposition and dissatisfaction. And law and custom approving heartily.

"What a thin veneer is the seeming of anything, I thought! How indifferent, and therefore merciless, are the forces that despite our notions and moods and dreams drive us all!

"In New York later I received some letters and a complaint from Rella to the effect that not only against her will was she being sent to a higher school but also being urged to marry a doctor whom she did not like; also a faint hint that if I would provide the means she might run away. But means at the time were not mine. More, for me at the moment life was wearing a face which made even love seem almost worthless. In fact, I was all but destroyed at the time, not only financially but physically—and so, not able to do anything. True, I wrote her in explanation but later ceased, knowing that only trouble could follow her through me.

"And later, of course, other women took Rella's place. As other men mine in her life. The unhappy union of which I was then half was finally broken up. Rella, sent to a relative in Texas, eventually married an oil speculator, whom I trust she loved. The last news I had of her was that after a visitation of some disease she had been left with a partially paralyzed eyelid, which completely marred her beauty. Also, that much of her wonderful hair had fallen out. And this before thirty."

. . . .

Verily, "what is man that thou art mindful of him? He cometh up as a flower, and is cut down. He fleeth as a shadow, and continueth not."

ERNESTINE

Ernestine

I THINK that the conclusions that troubled her most, and finally decided her upon her eventual step, were, first, that she had in some way mismanaged the opportunities that had been hers, and next, that life itself was a confusing gamble in which the cards were frequently marked and the dice weighted. She was, I am sure, a little confused and saddened by her eventual realization that the field she had espoused was engineered by men and women without real intelligence or decency or understanding, and with scarcely any traces of the stabilities upon which we must lean at times if we are to live at all. Also, I think that toward the last she failed to find in herself enough of those stabilities to warrant her continuing. She was too much inclined, possibly, to look for worth in others— too little to compel it in herself.

If I were less convinced that life itself is anything but a game, arranged for as well as motivated by the greedy, the arrogant, the lecherous, and the heartless, with dullards and beggars and nincompoops at the bottom as their tools and pawns, I would be prepared to assail the members of the joyous profession of which she was a part. There is little that is too sharp or uncomplimentary, I assure you, that might be said of them—mercenary, covetous, sycophantic, lax, dissolute, malevolent, brutal— But why go on? You may find lists that apply in Trent and Walker. Yet having said all this, I am still compelled to ask myself wherein they are so much worse than the members of any of the other professions that eventually and perforce, via related compulsions find themselves in authority in life. If any one or anything is to be indicted, let it be Life.

But to the tale itself.

The first time I saw Ernestine she was coming down the steps of the Sixth Avenue Elevated Station, at Eighth Street. She was very young, not more than eighteen or nineteen, and sensuously, and so disturbingly beautiful and magnetic. With her was an aspiring theatrical manager whom I knew,—the type that begins with a "little theater." He was showing her the Village, I presume, and his air was that of the impresario. Hers was that of a very young, and not very sophisticated, person who condescends to take notice of a domain offered for her inspection. There was a moment's pause while he introduced us, and then they were off. And yet, brief as was the contact, I could not but know that she was exceptional. The litheness and vigor of movement, which half denied a languorousness of temperament, which yet smote one! The health, and gayety, and poetry, and love of beauty! Something about her suggested two of the lines in one of a group of poems

later addressed to her by a writer and publisher who
for a time at least was enormously taken with her.

"I never taste the sweet exceeding thought
That you might love me, though I loved you
    not."

She was at this time interpreting something on the
legitimate stage, and her true habitat was the white
light region between 42nd and 59th Streets. But her
flutterings over the surface of the Greenwich Village
art sector of New York evoked not a little admiration
and enthusiasm. The young artists and playwrights
of the Village were, after a fashion, agog. She was
quite wonderful or so they said. One ought to see her.
Even the women of the Village admitted, if a little
grudgingly, that she had looks and a decided appeal,
for men anyhow.

At a party later I was a witness to this marked appeal and the fever of passion and yearning which she
evoked. Escorted by the same aspiring producer, she
had entered, and immediately the attention of the
men was centered upon her. Not that she was so
remarkably intelligent or artistically forceful as that
she had that indescribable something which all women
fear and envy—sex appeal. Her temperament as well
as her beauty was focal, and she knew it. Even while
some of the women were inclined to find fault with
her for one reason and another, they kept studying

her, while throughout she remained cool and beaming
—too cool, I thought at times, and too vain.

A famous critic of international repute—a student
of types and personalities—was sufficiently impressed
by her to enter on a long discussion of her type and
American girls in general. "Now there is this Ernestine
De Jongh," he said to me. "These American girls are
astonishing, really. They are not always so well
equipped mentally, but they have astounding sensual
and imaginative appeal as well as beauty and are able
to meet the exigencies of life in a quite satisfactory
manner, regardless of what Europe thinks; and that
is more than can be said for many of the women of
the other countries with which I happen to be familiar.
By that I mean that your American girl of this type
thinks and reasons as a woman, not as a man, viewing
the problems that confront her as a woman, studying
life from a woman's viewpoint and solving them as
only a woman can. She seems to realize, more than
do her sisters of almost any other country to-day, that
her business is to captivate and later dominate the
male, with all his special forces and intelligence, by hers,
and having done that she knows that she has bagged
the game. Now I do not count that as being inferior or
stupid. To me it is being effective."

While I was interested by this bit of philosophy,
which struck me as true, I was more interested by the
fact that this particular girl, at her age, should have
inspired it. For, distinctly, she was not intellectual, in

the best sense at least, and the critic in question was all but impervious to the befuddling force of beauty. His opinion confirmed my impression that after her fashion she was a personage, not a mere chemical assault upon the sensual hormones of the male.

About this time I began to learn something of her history. She was from the American northwest. Her father was a well-to-do dairyman in that region from which the Tillamook cheese comes. There was an elder sister in Seattle who had taken this younger one to live with her after she had been so fortunate as to marry a man of means herself. There Ernestine had come in contact with, and aspired to, the stage, as represented by private theatricals in which her sister happened to be interested at the time. And there she had eventually come to identify herself with a "little theater" movement. But, as she told me later, her father and mother were "old-fashioned and religious and very much opposed to the theater," and in order to avoid anger and ill-will on their part, she had for a long time concealed her interest in it. Finally, deciding to follow it as a profession, she had joined a touring company and changed her name—which was Swedish, I believe. There was the usual history connected with that venture, yet of not sufficient interest, or at least not sufficiently different, to merit a recital here.

I suspect that by then she had been in love more than once. Her manner was that of one who had learned to breast the stream of life with some little assurance. Plainly, she had come to realize the value and effect of her beauty, of which, as I say, she was markedly conscious.

It was perhaps six months or a year after I first met her that I began to hear of her as the mistress of a man of considerable reputation in the critical and liberal thought of the time. He was a poet, although of no great importance in that field. Personally, he interested me, not only as a character but as a man of force and appeal. For a period of years, beginning with his college days in New York, he had managed not only to sustain himself but others as well in the business of furthering one and another liberal or charitable cause—woman suffrage, child labor, a liberal, semi-radical paper, which he, or rather his patrons, financed. Also he had found time to write various books and essays full of fairly readable thoughts on poetry and reforms of various kinds. Incidentally, he was a handsome fellow, pleasingly cultivated in his ways and moods and without a trace of that aggressive, pushing, self-seeking need which too often one finds motivating those who are professedly interested in reforms.

That Ernestine understood him I doubt. More likely she was drawn by his virility, looks, charm and public repute—a man connected with the arts and intellectual matters. As she saw it, I think, it was rather exceptional for a man to be a writer and a critic and a poet all at once—one who could get his name into the papers and be looked up to by a number of beginners as a

personage. In addition, he was really good-looking
and gay. Apart from that, I doubt that she was
able to share his finer moods. And yet she had a
kind of crude reverence for them, as time was to show
—a reverence, indeed, for everything connected with
the arts and those who achieved in them, without quite
knowing why. That she was obtuse to all phases of his
character I do not mean to imply. She understood him
well in some ways, as was made plain by the manner
in which she could set forth his methods and his own
attitude toward himself—descriptions, in the main,
very penetrating and illuminating.

Once she said to me: "I never saw such a person as
Varn." (Varn Kinsey was his name.) "When he wants
to be nice I think he can be the nicest person in the
world. He has such an air. And he thinks so well of
himself—not in a silly but rather in a reverential way,—
as though he felt himself called by God or someone to fulfill a great duty of some kind. You know
the sort of person I mean, perhaps. He looks upon
everthing he thinks, or says, or does, as important.
What other people think and say and do does not
appeal to him so much. And he never looks upon
any one else, whoever he may be, as more than an
equal, if as much. For that reason, perhaps, he is
always able to get money out of rich people for any
cause in which he actually believes. I never saw such
a person for finding people interested in the things
he is interested in, and then playing up to them. I

wouldn't say that he is a toady, exactly, but he can always manage to talk to them, especially rich women, in a way that makes them willing to help him. Once he gets the money for any cause, though, he usually leaves to other people the work for which the money has been secured, resting and taking the largest salary for his pains. He used to say that he had done enough when he raised the money.

"And of course he is always surrounded by a lot of minor people who look up to him as a leader and who do the things he feels he hasn't time for. As for himself, he reads, and writes essays and poetry, and gets himself interviewed from time to time in connection with the things he is supposed to be doing. I suppose he actually does render some kind of intellectual service to the causes he is supposed to further. He used to argue that the mere use of his name and the way he looked after things enabled him to get the money for the things he did. Also he added that it was necessary for him to live well and keep up appearances in order to help the causes he was interested in."

This is one of those interpretations she could provide so freely after she had known Varn for four years and which caused me to think of her as intelligent. She analyzed him then as from time to time afterwards she was able to analyze others.

When Ernestine came into Kinsey's life he was fifteen years her senior and married to a woman of

ability and charm who was a painter and illustrator.
But shortly after this meeting there came rumors of
trouble between him and his wife. They were no
longer so much together as they had been. They were
quarrelsome. Where formerly Varn had been an arresting figure at Mrs. Kinsey's teas and affairs, now he
was absent. Meanwhile he was being seen with
Ernestine. I myself was once a witness of a happy
dinner they took together. It was in one of those many-
roomed, semi-theatrical cafés which abound north of
Forty-second Street and it was the crowded hour between seven and eight. They came in while I was
dining with a friend and found a corner near us, but
without noting that I or any one else was near them.
They were too much engrossed in each other. Once
seated, and before ordering, they fell into a deep and
plainly affectionate conversation. So impressed was he
by her beauty that he seemed to devour her with his
eyes. And she, conscious of the spell that her charm
had cast, sat back and allowed him to gaze upon her,
bestowing upon him from time to time the most
ravishing of smiles. And once he seized both her hands
in his and held them while he gazed into her eyes.

"There is a man," commented my companion, "who
most certainly is in love. It is charming, don't you
think? He seems to view her poetically. He is obsessed
with her beauty."

I agreed. Also, as I observed, more than one of those
dining there glanced at them interestedly.

I should add that time proved that this infatuation was genuine, for he divorced his wife. And though he never married Ernestine, there was a live and close and seemingly happy relationship between them. He became conspicuously devoted to her, and for several years thereafter one scarcely saw one without the other. And yet I gathered from many sources at the time, and later, that she was by no means an affectionate slave. Rather, it was he who could scarcely sleep because of her.

Kinsey and myself, having little in common, rarely met; nor, except on rare occasions, did I encounter Ernestine. She was always busy with her stage work. But of her life and moods in connection with him and herself I heard not a little from many who were close to them. While they were happy for the first year or so, (and that was the period in which the series of poems exalting her were written by him; they are still extant), afterwards there had begun to appear difficulties in connection with her work, or rather her interest in a new form of it. For just at that time a new type of opportunity, the motion picture, was coming into public favor, and with it newer and sharper conditions governing the rise of stars in that particular field. One had to be the mistress of somebody—director, producer, owner or backer—or so it was said. Nevertheless the opportunity for the concomitant enormous financial returns was being grasped and responded to by attractive and ambitious girlhood the country over.

I heard a great deal at the time of the interest a certain picture producer of great wealth and notoriety was taking in Ernestine, and the interest that she was taking—not so much in him as a man or a possible lover as in the power he possessed of rapidly furthering the career of any one in whom he chanced to be interested, in this new field which he represented —(the Arabian lure of the movies in those days). And much against Kinsey's will and wish, as it now appeared, Ernestine had already ventured upon several screen tests in one and another of the new studios in New York, which were then mere floors or lofts in ordinary loft buildings. A new director of rumored ability who was then operating in a loft in Union Square, had cast her for several minor rôles, which proved to her own satisfaction that she might shine in this new field if she applied herself and if opportunity favored her.

But there was the rub. For Varn Kinsey would have none of it—that is, not with himself as a factor in her life. A bachelor of arts and inclined by education and training to look to the more serious productions of the stage for anything histrionically worthy, he was not in the least interested in the pretensions of those who were destined to feed the multitude with what it could grasp. In fact, he disliked motion pictures, and above all he was opposed to the conditions of advancement as those conditions were now being revealed to him. Any talk of the fat and powerful masters in that world who were holding tempting morsels of fame and wealth before such aspirants as Ernestine was likely to inflame and enrage him. As long as she was connected with the legitimate stage in New York, where nightly he could find her—well, that was different. As for sharing her time at all hours and in all places with motion picture directors who had "locations" and such to propose—that was something else again. He would leave her if she attempted it.

Came finally a certain picture producer, part owner of one of the great film companies, who was much impressed by what he had seen and heard of Ernestine. Because of what he could do for her if he chose, (I heard this from herself later), he expected her to take a great personal interest in him, and in spite of the crudity of his approach, and because of the great power he represented, Ernestine was interested, because, as she said later, she was almost abnormally ambitious. A craze for fame was driving her—fame and applause —and so, while evading him as gracefully as possible, still, because of what he might do for her, she sought to cultivate his friendship. But when intimation of this reached Kinsey's ears, there was trouble. At the time— and not from her later—I heard of a storm which caused him to depart from his studio and take quarters in a hotel; also, that at three o'clock of another morning, later, she had followed him there and was all but beaten for her pains. After that came heartaches and reunions and separations, until finally there came a last separation. For a long time neither was to be seen about their old haunts. Ernestine, as I heard, had departed for studio work somewhere. Then, alone, Kinsey returned to the quiet and studious world that had known him. Obviously, he was too vigorous and interesting a man to share the favors of any woman, however attractive, with another, and that was what success in this work for Ernestine appeared to mean.

Some six or eight months later I was interested to see posted about New York on the billboards an announcement of a new screen drama or romance, (one of the earliest of the six-reel productions), and with the name of Ernestine De Jongh as the star. In relatively modest type, as producer, appeared the name of the man who had been so engrossed in her the year before. Curiously enough, I had meanwhile met this man. He was one of those persons who thinks that the answer to everything—quite everything—lies in wealth and power. He was blond, red-blooded, dynamic, of the merchant and organizing type, contemptuous of rivals and of the pretensions of others. Trade, the plastering of his name here and there as owner or producer of this, that and the other, the possession of pretty women—such were his ambitions. How Ernestine De Jongh, fresh from the allurements of such a poetically-minded person as Kinsey, could have turned to a man of this type was. from one point of view, and yet from another not so very, difficult to understand. While she admired Varn Kinsey's intellectual reputation, still more did she love finery and fame, and these the newcomer had to offer. So, I thought when I heard this, she has succumbed after all. Kinsey was not strong enough to hold her. There must be, I decided, a coarse streak there after all. The lure of fame! The hope of distinction! And in that field!

A week or two later I stopped in to see the picture, because I was interested to see the type of thing she was doing and whether her ambition in this direction was as justly grounded as her stage work, or whether this was a case of a medium prepared to flatter the vanity of one not legitimately suited to the work in hand. To my surprise and interest, the picture was entirely satisfactory, as such things go, and Ernestine also. The story? Oh, well, it was movie-esque but very well suited to a girl of her beauty and charm, and built around just such a girl as herself. Its *premier pas* was in such a world as she must have come from—an old farm home. And she was pictured as a simple country maid, dreaming of love and some impossible earthly supremacy. There was the customary country lover, whom she favored, and the city magnate who eventually realized her worth and gave her her chance. There was the usual romantic ending—a return to the old home, only to find that the one-time love had fled also and had scored a success scarcely less exceptional than her own. Whether they were brought together after the approved movie pattern I do not recall.

But what interested me was that from a technical point of view the thing was very well done, and the support given her all that could be expected of those who labor in that very artificial field. Indeed, the whole thing seemed to suggest a sincere effort on the part of her sponsor to provide her with a proper medium. That meant then that he was really interested in her. More, it seemed to me that she bade fair to prove acceptable to a large public. She was beautiful, and no expense had been spared to make her costumes and settings as striking as possible. After all, I thought, she may have chosen wisely, from a practical point of view, anyhow. This man appears to be sufficiently interested in her to do as well by her as could be expected.

A year or two after this an actor I knew who had been to the west coast in connection with a screen contract returned to report a fascinating development in that part of the world. Los Angeles itself was not so much of a city—rather a Methodist settlement where formerly had been sand and cactus—but one of its suburbs, Hollywood, was certainly a new kind of thing. Pepper and palm trees and flowers had made it into a kind of paradise. And there were marvelous skies and mountains, and automobile roads splendidly laid, to say nothing of a coast line dotted with beaches. A new and different kind of cottage—

the California bungalow—modeled very much on Japanese lines—abounded, and in them dwelt the most startling and reckless and extravagant of a new type of Thespian, the motion picture star, with a salary which made the salaries of the most successful of the "legitimate" workers seem low and small. A world of swagger, and bluff, and fine feathers, was to be seen in surroundings which would inspire a poet.

Apropos of all this he suddenly added: "Did you ever meet Ernestine De Jongh who used to live here in New York?"

"Sure."

"Well, you should see her place out there. She has one of the most charming little homes I ever saw. Not large, but different, and suited to that climate. She has a walled court, with flowers and a fountain in it at the back, and the most delightfully furnished rooms in the house proper. They are Japanesy, with windows and doors that slide sidewise into the wall and open level with porches and walks. And she has a Japanese cook and maid, as well as a gardener. She was working on a new picture while I was there."

Well done, I thought. That shows how easily beauty united with a little practical sense triumphs in this world.

And then the conversation turned to the movie magnate whose interest had proved Ernestine's opportunity.

"He's a grandee of sorts in the movie world out

there, you know. He recently built himself a gorgeous residence in a place called Beverly Hills, which is just west of Hollywood. He's married, you know, and has a child."

"Is he?" I inquired, wondering, for I had thought that possibly . . .

Then he gave me the name of the actress whom he had married some six or seven years before.

"Well, what about Ernestine?" I asked.

"Oh, you know how it is," he replied. "Those fellows at the top in the game take their women rather lightly. I haven't a doubt that he cared for her at first. At least he gave her her start in pictures, and she has done fairly well. But those things never last, you know. A fellow like that meets too many beautiful aspirants all the time. And as things are now, it isn't very hard to launch one or two of them now and then. If she makes good, very well. If she doesn't, in the course of time she has to fall in behind those who do. The slate is wiped clean when they give a girl an opportunity. I think, all told, that Ernestine has nothing to complain of. She's been in three pictures, and is doing another now. He's out of it, however. I hear he's interested in . . ." and he gave me another current name.

Recalling the individual as I knew him and recalling also the nature of her attitude toward him at first, I could not help but feel that apart from financial or practical considerations the loss could not have been so much. She had probably never cared for him in an emotional sense. On the other hand, I could not help but feel that the relationship with Kinsey must have been of a different character. There are orders and orders of men and women. Some of them possess a sensitivity, a refinement, which takes and retains impressions deeply. Others are adamantine, incapable of a scratch. And others are water, incapable of retaining any impression.

The thing dwelt with me. I still saw Kinsey about, alone as a rule, a book or two under his arm and always busy with those "reforms" which seemed to afford him such a good living. And then, three years later, I journeyed to the west coast, and under circumstances which tended to bring me in contact with the very element about which my actor friend had been talking. Not that I was personally connected with the film industry in any way—it was from contact with others that I heard and saw a great deal. In truth, I had occasion to study the thing at first hand, but this is no place to record my impressions. In the main they would not be fit to print anyhow! The tinsel! The arrogance! The vainglory! The asininity! The waste! The fol-de-rol! The rush of a little temporary prosperity to the head! Vulgarians, mental lightweights posing as geniuses, creators, heirs to the Bard of Avon himself! And surrounding and overflowing all this, downright gross and savage and defiant vulgarity!

In my youth, as a schoolboy, I used to read and

vaguely wonder at the nature of the pagan orgy. Stray bits concerning the florid passions and satiations of Sidon and Tyre and Greece and Rome and Antioch had blown my way, and I had wondered about them. Plainly, I argued then, in my innocence and ignorance, such things were gone forever. The like of them would never come again. The world would not tolerate even a trace of such things as had been in those olden days. Yet, in the flower-covered bungalows of Hollywood and its environs, at that time, behind closed doors, and with obsequious assistant-directors, camera men, masters and mistresses of wardrobe, alleged scenarists, and actors, all pandering to the elect as represented by directors and stars and managers generally, what nights! Representative of an older, and presumably concluded, world. I doubt if either novelist or historian has ever painted scenes more suggestive of what the ancients are supposed to have known than were here visible to the living eye. Drunkenness, lechery, and gluttony were the order of the night, and the following morning, for that matter. Gestures and dances and erotically-worded appeals, calculated to urge the lagging or to hearten the half-hearted. Promiscuous pawing. Indiscriminate and public caressing. Actors, directors, stars and stockholders all united in an orgy of self-satiation, and without the danger of publicity. And on the part of those anxious to succeed in pictures at almost any price, a desire not to offend. And over it all a kind of compulsion arising from not only the power but the will of those in authority to bring about just such effects as were here being achieved.

This may sound like an exaggerated picture, but it is not. And it is entirely probable that power and affluence, wherever these same chance to be achieved, ever tend to license after the manner here indicated. You are to remember that commercial power and affluence to a fantastic degree had descended upon many who had never previously known either.

And of this world was this girl, now something of a personage. I will not say that she was an enthusiastic member of it, because I do not know. Nevertheless, she was distinctly of the mind or mood to countenance all that she saw here for the sake of the advantage it might bring her financially. Then, more than now, the grandees and magnificoes of this realm—the male portion at least, to say nothing of a heavy percentage of the women themselves—were determined to satiate themselves at any cost. Rules were even made that no young married woman of any shade of loyalty to her vows need apply for advancement in this field, and no unmarried woman of any great beauty or physical appeal need apply unless willing to submit herself, harem-wise, to the managers and directors, and even principals. For in nearly all cases at this time the principals were able to say with whom, or without whom, they would work. And if a girl were young and attractive she had to be hail-fellow-well-met with every Tom, Dick and Harry from prop-boy and office-

scullion to director, casting director and president.
She had to "troop," be "a regular fellow." The fact
that Ernestine for several years was a figure in this
local scene would—so it seemed to me at the time—
indicate that in part at least she did as the Romans did.
Still, one may seem at times and yet not actually be—
though I met her at one of these bungalow parties at
the "home" of a famous director one evening and was
a witness to much that I have just described.

The entertainment had been in progress for several
hours when the group of which I made one entered.
Plainly there had been a steady flow of liquors. Quite
all of those present were the worse for what they had
already consumed. Girls and men—orchids and fashion
plates—were here in number, dancing, singing, talking, or rallying one another about things with which
they were familiar. Occasionally they disappeared,
pair by pair, into one of the numerous minor rooms,
only to reappear after a time smiling and defiant.
Amazingly frank and frankly insulting questions were
asked and answered. "If it isn't little . . . ! And only
three months ago she was so shy!" "Come see, fellows!
Look in here! And drunk, too!" "Is it your idea,
Clarice, that wearing so little will make you more
enticing?" "Who's the beauty D . . . has brought
with her to-night?" (This from a girl star of national
and later international fame.) "Bring your girl friend
over, D . . . and introduce me, will you? We'll put
sawdust on the floor and liquor on the table." "Say,

Willard, you're needed in here. You're the only one
will do, it seems. . . ." Assort and arrange and apply
such things for yourself. Your fancy cannot go very
far amiss.

But, as I say, Ernestine De Jongh was there, and
before her was one of those large, bull-like "heroes"
of the film world, in *de rigueur* evening clothes but
much the worse for liquor. He was taking such frank
liberties with her as I would never have dreamed possible in her case, and she was passing the same off with
a half-intoxicated smile, protecting herself as best she
could but not very forcefully at that. Thinking she
might recognize me and not wishing to embarrass
her, I turned away, and after a time left without
actually speaking to her.

But having seen her again I was interested to learn
of her state after these several years. She had looked
about as attractive as ever, though not quite so young,
with a way and air and a ready humor that was pleasing enough. On inquiry I learned that financially she
was about as well placed as ever, having a car and the
bungalow and considerable work as leading female
support to one star and another, male and female.
Yet she herself was no longer starred. A competent
interpreter of such rôles as were assigned to her, still
she was placed second to one and another movie queen
or king of probably no greater acting ability than herself. Why? By more than one casting director I was
told that while she was a competent actress, still her

coloring, which was dark, and her height, about five feet seven inches, were not in the mode just at the moment. Besides, she was looked upon as rather serious, more so than most of the stars then shining, and directors desired and required types which were all that youth and beauty meant but without much brains. They liked to provide the "thought." "They say that when they think too much, or even a little, they lose that girlish something which is very much in demand at this time," one casting director explained. I am convinced that he spoke the truth. The annual movie output of that period should attest the soundness of his observation, I think.

Yet from time to time she was appearing in current successes, such as they were, and at a salary of three hundred and fifty to five hundred dollars a week. There was a film comedian of some standing and considerable intelligence who was considered to be one of her best friends. In fact, there was a small circle of semi-intellectuals in that region who paid no little attention to her and with whom she was engaged socially when she was not working.

During all of a year after my arrival, just one incident brought her to mind again. That was the sight of Kinsey one spring evening strolling along Hollywood Boulevard. He was dressed correctly for Hollywood—white flannel trousers, light silk shirt, a short, belted, gray coat, and no hat. Under his arm were a couple of books and a light overcoat. (The evenings are always cool in Hollywood, winter and summer.) The thought came to me that there must have been a reunion, else why his presence here? I hoped so.

And then one day, perhaps as much as a month or six weeks later, I received a letter from Ernestine. She had seen my name in a paper, as I guessed, and something that was said caused her to be interested. Or perhaps it was Kinsey who had spoken of me. At any rate, it was an artfully worded invitation to meet some one who was most anxious to see me and who was presuming upon her ancient and brief contact with me for the opportunity. I could read or feel that there was some-thing she wanted at this time. But what? The com-paratively recent glimpse of Kinsey caused me to go back in thought to him. Psychically I caught something —the thought that maybe there had been an attempt on her part toward a reconciliation and that possibly, the thing having come to nothing, she had decided to use me in some way, possibly as a flag or a rag of a provoking shade to wave in his face. Could that be? I wondered.

Curious as to the import of this, I looked her up and found her in her very charming bungalow. It was a lovely place, really a tasteful and colorful thing, and suggestive of a genuine love of beauty in her. After my one sight of her at the party I was prepared to find her sensibilities hardened, but this was not the case. She was gracious, tactful, artful, not unlike her old self, and yet more interesting because more experienced. She told me much concerning the lives of movie celebrities, their interests, relative positions, moods, successes, failures. I was not only interested in but struck by a subtle undercurrent in her talk which seemed to suggest, if not actually blazon, a certain dissatisfaction with herself and the world in which she found herself. It was this, that—so hectic and yet in the main so shallow and vapid. After a little while she began talking earnestly of Kinsey and the old life. In short, becoming interested, she proceeded to outline carefully just why she had left him. He was too dictatorial, or was tending to become so, in connection with what she did, her work especially. All the while, though, she was plainly manifesting the keenest interest in him, yet without seeming to wish to do so. It was noticeable. He had been out here, she said, in connection with a great folk drama which was being planned and for which—the money-raising and staging ends of it, at least—she had ventured to suggest his name. Not that she wished to reëstablish the old relationship. Distinctly she hinted the reverse of this— but rather because he was so well fitted for the task and she could be of service to the enterprise and him also. He had come and gone and she had not seen him more than two or three times. He was as interesting as ever, but of course . . . And then she gave me to understand that the old relation was done for, and that she had definitely willed it to be so. I wondered.

As for the picture magnate, there was never a word which could be construed as an admission that there had ever been anything but a strictly business arrangement between them. He, or rather some members of the organization he controlled, had seen her in some of the plays in which she had appeared in the east and had been interested in her possibilities on the screen. Later he had sent for her and had offered her the title rôle in one of his productions. "I know that some people think differently," she emphasized, "but that was all there was to it. During the first two years I starred in four of his productions, then another company sent for me and I did some work for them. Since then I have been free-lancing, as most of the people in this work are." And she gave me an interesting account of the drawbacks that attend a five- or ten-year contract, assuming that one were so foolish as to make one at the opening of one's career. The one point that remained a point was that by these varying organizations, and since those first days, she had never been starred. I could see and feel that she had sold herself for "a mess of potash," as one of Thackeray's amusing characters used to say.

Followed a number of meetings during the course of which she gave me my first keen insight into the type of woman who was pressing to success in so many of the "sweet sixteen" romances of the hour. There was but one answer, of course, in quite every such case, though she never said so in so many words. Making due allowance for such few celebrities as came to their positions because of a tremendous ability manifested before ever they were called to the screen, they were mostly female adventurers, if not libertines, and, to a very marked extent, wasters. They had to sell themselves to the highest bidders or fall, and quite uniformly they sold themselves. They had no essential refinement; they were suffering from complexes relating to dress, beauty, and screen recognition, to say nothing of the personal approval of men they considered marvelous accomplishers of this, that and the other, yet who, in the main, were bounders and dubs and wasters like themselves. The substance of her observations, along with those of others, is to be found in a series of articles published by me in one of the screen publications of the time. All that she reported could not be published, of course, owing to censorship limitations.

But it was not these things, irritating and discouraging as they were, but herself in relation to them and to such ideals as at any time she may have possessed, that interested me. She knew this and resented, I am sure, the worst phases of her career, and yet set up a purely material defense. Her bungalow, her clothes, her car, her friendships in this world, depended upon her accepting the conditions as she found them, you see, and more, pretending to like them, if actually she did not. I suspected, and am sure that I am right, that for some time she did like them, captivated by the flare and show and animal spirits of this realm.

Her appearance at the party I attended indicated as much. Later, like the prodigal son, having had her fill of this particular kind of husk, her mood tended to revert, for a time, anyhow, to that other world of which Kinsey was a fair representative. She was overawed, if not actually captivated, by the mental and artistic prestige which Kinsey and that world had represented to her and which this present world of hers did not.

And after a very little time, by the uses to which she attempted to put these contacts with me, I could see that such was the case. Despite all she had to say about the characters and methods of one and another of these seekers and beginners, to say nothing of those who were already successful, still, like every other person in that decidedly weedy field, she was endeavoring to get ahead herself as best she might. I began to see that one of her principal sins was to overawe some of these celebrities with her connections and contacts in the Kinsey realm. Also that, after a time I was likely to be used to the same end. That is, being used as a stalking horse or decoy for another. She could scarcely suggest a walk, a drive, or a dinner, or a quiet hour's chat anywhere, without having as an ulterior purpose an ending-up at some café or club or bungalow or apartment where one was likely to meet one or another of the "bigwigs" and under such circumstances as were most certain to reflect credit upon her. And on such occasions she was almost insistent upon introductions and "Who's Who" explana-

tions which could only prove disagreeable. More than
once I was compelled to make it plain that I abhorred
promiscuous introductions, especially in this field. I had
no stomach for such maneuvering as she was indulging
in. Our friendship must rest upon simpler and less
conspicuous things if it was to endure. This, as one
hears it phrased these days, she accepted in principle
but not in fact. And yet, in spite of all her faults, I
liked her as a type and example and made strenuous
efforts not to prove too irritable or inconvenient.

But it was not to be. In spite of all hints, and even
definite objections, there was this tendency on nearly
every occasion that we met. Irritated one afternoon by
the sudden descent of a group when it had been plainly
understood that there was to be no one, I left, and that
in the face of the suddenly assembled company. Thereafter, our contacts were not so numerous, accidental
mostly, in the streets or restaurants.

But during the time that I was with her I was really
fascinated by the picture she presented of one who
keenly realized the defects of the world in which she
found herself and because of that I was troubled at the
thought of an ideal implanted in her by Kinsey which
she was unwilling to relinquish. Yet, at the same time,
as I could see, she was still anxious to unite the two
fields in some way, to make herself something in both.
Once she brought out a book of poems written by
Kinsey and showed me those she liked most. They
were obviously about her and it was easy to see that she

was still fascinated by the tribute. She spoke of his genius, his essential culture and superiority—so different from those with whom she was now associated. In the room also was a portrait of her by an artist friend of Kinsey's, made at the time that they were still together. The painter had caught not a little of that remarkable appeal that was hers then. By contrast I was forced to note that after a lapse of about six years she had coarsened and hardened to some extent, and yet not so much as to make it disturbingly apparent. There was still about her at times, especially when she was made up to go out, that seeming freshness and youthfulness and inexperience which had characterized her when I first saw her, and which no doubt she sought consciously to retain. When she inquired if I thought she had changed any, I gallantly lied.

At the same time I was compelled to note that in so far as her speech, manners, and thoughts were concerned, especially when she was seriously engaged in conversation and not posing, many of the marks of her later sophistication were apt to become apparent. Little things like an expression, verbal or facial, or a word of reference to a place or person (such as the rooms of a wretched director whom I knew and who was subsequently debarred from any connection with studios anywhere) threw an all but searing light upon her. I could see that in spite of anything she might say or do, she had drunk deep at this well, and now, curiously enough, was ashamed of the meaner aspects of it all. In so far as one might guess from her conversation, she had never been to any such party as the one described. (She never knew, of course, that I had actually seen her at one.) She wanted to be the woman whom Kinsey had idealized. That finer poetic something which was in him, and which she had once known and recognized, she now craved far more than anything else that could have come to her. At times there was something poignant in her references to him and the life they had known together.

About that time there came the first and most serious slump in the motion picture industry. For one or another of the various reasons assigned at the time—overproduction, importation of foreign films, extravagance on the part of those engaged in production, the determination of Wall Street to force a reduction of expenses and smaller salaries upon all principals, a falling off of attendance at movie theaters—production all but ceased for something over a year. Such salaries as were paid were cut to one-half or less. Perhaps as many as forty thousand workers of all sorts and descriptions were most disastrously affected for more than a year. Literally scores of directors, who posed as dictators and masters and had built for themselves imposing homes and strutted about with the air of princes, were compelled to close or dispose of these either permanently or temporarily. Stars, staresses, and starettes, of much or little repute, to say nothing of actors and actresses of the second lead, "heavies," "vamps," assistant leads, ingénues, camera men, assistant directors, scenarists, and so on, were compelled to abandon, for the time being anyhow, their almost luxurious fields of employment, and wait, making the best of a dreary period during which their incomes ceased. Literally hundreds of the most artistically fashioned and luxuriously furnished bungalows and homes of those connected with this industry were either offered for rent or after a time the leases and contents sold outright. The fifty or more once humming studios of that western metropolis stood silent and idle. Toward the end of the year absolute panic seemed to seize upon nearly all who had been waiting so patiently for some signs of resumption, and by degrees they moved into other fields—vaudeville, the legitimate stage, designing, dressmaking, millinery, beauty parlors,—in fact, everything or anything that offered. By the beginning of the second year nearly all had returned to the east, hoping to sustain themselves in some way there until better times should come again. Indeed, a year and a half had passed before there was even a shadow of a change in this very depressed field.

During this time I saw very little of the woman whose career had thus far interested me. Once, in front of one of the larger studios, which was practically inoperative, I chanced in passing to see her and another actress just leaving the place. But there was no motor car in sight. This was about eleven o'clock in the morning, and the absence of a car in her case at that

time struck me as odd. During the days of her prosperity I knew that she never ventured anywhere unless
in her own or another's car or a taxi. Later, meeting
her upon the principal thoroughfare, I was told by her
that she had been compelled to give up her home and
her car because of conditions in the business. She
had, however, she said, taken a rather charming apartment elsewhere, which I was to come and see. She was
living much more simply now—every one was. It had
not been possible for her to maintain the old scale of
living for some time past. No one knew when things
would be better.

I did stop at her new place one day, and found it
pleasing enough as to location, though far from being
as attractive as her bungalow. The latter had represented an outlay of perhaps seven or eight thousand a
year. This might have cost as much as fifteen hundred,
furnished—no more. From a brief talk with her I
gathered that she was dubious as to her future. She
was apparently alone and at the time not interested in
any one, unless, perhaps, it was Kinsey, who was no
longer interested in her. The tendency of those who
planned and directed pictures, she complained, was
ever away from those who were proficient, if aging,
however slightly, and toward those who were young
and inexperienced. Inexperience, where joined with
youth and charm, though not necessarily ability, was at
a premium with most of the dominant directors because they could use and mold these aspirants to their

will and mood, taking all the credit for the result. Besides, here was this amazing slump, or cessation, the end of which no one could foresee. She hinted that she, too, might sell the furnishings of her house, (which all this time had been carried on a lease), and return east, where, of course, the legitimate stage was her only hope. Nevertheless, she still continued to carry a certain air of optimism and make-believe security such as is affected by most in that world.

Just about this time—a week or ten days before, I think—the papers had reported the death by suicide of a girl we both knew—one of the pleasing figures of the world of which Ernestine and Kinsey had been a part. The life and experiences of this girl are too long and too complicated to inject here; they would make a novel, and a powerful one. The thing that interested me, and that I foolishly commented upon at the time, was that particular atom's very courageous outlook on life and death. More than once I had heard her say, and this I now idly related, that she counted the years from sixteen to twenty-eight as the very best of those granted to women. After them came, more than likely, the doldrums. Come what might, her purpose was to spend these years as she chose. At the end . . . well . . . And it was so, at twenty-nine, that she had ended herself—with a sleeping potion—after an almost fantastic career.

Ernestine appeared to be intensely interested. She drummed on the table with her fingers as we talked, and after we had concluded seemed to be thinking deeply.

"I think she was right," she said, after a time. "I believe in that. I despise age myself. Any one who had been really beautiful and knows what it means will understand."

I looked at her curiously. There was something intense and, I might say, predetermined in the way she spoke.

. . . .

I saw nothing more of her. The next time I passed that way a "For Rent" sign posted in one of the windows of the apartment stared at me. So she has gone, I thought, and stopped to see if her name was still on the plate. But it had been removed. Later, I heard that she had sold all her furniture and gone back to New York. Three months later, the series of articles the data for which she had largely furnished having begun in one of the magazines, and the newspapers having reprinted some of the most startling and disturbing facts detailed therein, I received a laconic "Thanks" by wire, and so I understood that she had been reading them and approved. But after that I heard nothing until one morning all of the Los Angeles daily papers carried an extended dispatch from New York covering the suspected suicide in Greenwich Village of one Ernestine De Jongh, quondam screen star, who, in an apartment which formerly she had occupied while connected with the legitimate stage in New

York, had turned on the gas. No data as to a probable cause was available. It was true that she had been connected with pictures and that these were now in the doldrums, but it was not believed that she was in need of money. Her family, so it was said, was well-to-do, and had been notified. No letters or least scrap of writing had been found. It was not known that she was in love with anybody, though it had been rumored recently that she was engaged to a certain famous star. Subsequently he denied this, insisting that they had been merely friends.

But I thought I understood. Somehow also I thought I understood why she had returned to the scene of her older, and possibly happier, days with Kinsey. Or did I? At any rate, there she went, and there they found her. I never learned what, if any, part he played in that latest development. No one seemed to know that he had played any. It was said that he was very sad.

RONA MURTHA

Rona Murtha

HER name brings to mind a delightful spring and summer early in the last decade of the last century and a very tall office building in the financial heart of New York. At that time I was a mere beginner in the world of letters, having essayed but a few articles and one or two short stories.

And at that time, as novices sometimes will, I had made friends and common cause with a young writer of about my own age and predilections who had recently arrived in New York. He was brilliant, good-looking, semi-idealistic, in philosophy at least, but useless for almost any practical purpose in life, and yet— and perhaps for that reason—most interesting to me. As I saw him then and see him now, he was a dreamer of dreams, a spinner of fine fancies, a lover of impossible romances which fascinated me by their very impossibility. Also he was jolly, generous, a lover of life and of play, mostly play as I later came to think. His weakest and most irritating trait was a vaulting egotism which caused him to imagine, first, that he was as great a thinker and writer as had ever appeared; second, that he was at the same time practical, a man of the world, a man of affairs. Let him but give his solemn attention to any muddle and it must come straight. Let him but think seriously, and every philosophic as well as practical riddle was solved. In short, he loved to direct and control as well as argue. Because I liked him much, as did nearly every one else with whom he came in contact, I was inclined to let him have his way in everything. He was too delightful and interesting not to humor.

But, as I soon discovered in talking to him about his past, not a few things that he had hitherto attempted to solve or set right for himself had gone wrong. At twenty-two, for instance, he had married a most charming and intelligent girl, and at twenty-three he was the father of a child and the putative bread-winner of the family and director of its destinies. But in a Shelley-esque manner, (which had he ever achieved great repute would have been forgiven him), he had walked away and left both to shift for themselves. But to be duly truthful in the matter, his wife was essentially capable and better able to take care of herself than he was of taking care of himself. He was always one of those idealists who needs some one to look after him.

At the time we met I had a home to which he could resort, a table at which he could dine, and some little money to pay for outings here and there. Also I had entry to several magazines. So we lived, dined, walked, talked together. Quite everything that he did and said and thought was right with me, even though I knew at times that it was really quite wrong—for instance, the way he neglected his wife and child. But affection will blur if not obliterate a great many defects. And so close did this union become that nearly all of our literary work was done together, side by side, he advising with me and I with him. Nearly all of our week-ends and holidays were joint affairs, my wife being quite as fond of Winnie (Vlasto was his last name) as was I. Together one summer, then, we visited his old home on the Meshant River in Michigan, romping and playing an entire month or more. Indeed, spiritually, or in all the things that relate to mind, beauty, art, we were brothers, and according to Winnie, destined throughout all the dry and trying days this side the grave to aid one the other. Ah, yes! Even now I can hear his voice, see his blue eyes, sense the vagrom charm of his all too vagrom dreams—the mere feel of him, his invariable optimism and gayety as set over against my all too solemn and personally disquieting contemplation of the fate of man. He had a way of making so much out of nothing. Money? Pooh! It was for those who no longer had the capacity to enjoy life. Mind was the key to every secret and every delight. Love and delight —these came to those who were made for them, preordained by their very chemism to enjoy them. Did I not know that? Alas, all too well I did. It was the hardest phase and face of the structure of life for me to contemplate, or for him either at such moments as he was compelled to face the same.

But Winnie had developed what he labeled "a doctrine of happiness," about which he talked and wrote much, but which was little more, as I saw it, than a kind of self-salving, soul-salving way of escaping a too galling routine of duty. For the first rule of his new, cheerful doctrine was to be happy oneself, regardless of others and come what might; only in order to give it a somewhat more humane look it was explained that by so doing one conveyed happiness and sunshine to others—a doctrine which struck me as a contradiction in terms. Notwithstanding said doctrine, he was by no means so utterly happy himself always, albeit doing his best to believe that he was. There were his wife and child, for instance, for whom he was not providing, and in connection with whom he was salving himself with all sorts of sophistications. He was faithful, was he not? And it was his plan to do something for them as soon as he had the necessary means. And his wife was really a better business man than he was. Which was true enough.

As for that faithfulness which he sometimes offered in extenuation, well, he was fascinated by women—almost any young, pretty, and intelligent girl—and he could not see why he should not be allowed to make friends and play with them. And most women he met were inclined to agree with him. Yet I honestly think that up to this time quite all of his relations with women were platonic. Only so pagan and pantheistic by nature was he, and so instinctively resentful of all chains, ties and obligations—those binding him to his wife and child as much as any—that it was difficult for these relations to remain wholly simple, to the eye at least. He could grow so affectionate. Even the normally conservative woman appeared to wish to indulge him.

Having said so much, let us leave him at this point and turn to another scene and situation.

One day, having completed a short article, I put it in my pocket and set out to find a typist. Another errand taking me into a certain large office building in the financial district, I saw, in the lobby opposite a bank of elevators, a gilt-framed sign which read:

RONA MURTHA
Court Proceedings
Law Stenography—Conventions
Commercial and Literary Typing
Mimeographing, Multigraphing

———

16th Floor

Bethinking me of my story, I proceeded to the sixteenth floor, where I encountered a young and quite attractive woman who interested me not a little from the point of view of alertness, awareness, and efficiency. She was, as I casually guessed, in the vicinity of twenty-four or twenty-five years of age; small, graceful, and carefully dressed in a close-fitting, tailor-made suit, white collars and cuffs, a bright tie, and sturdy little shoes. In the left pocket of her shirtwaist were various pens and pencils. Her ample supply of bluish-black hair was parted over one temple and then manipulated into a graceful roll at the back.

But what interested me almost as much as herself was the apparent magnitude of the commercial industry of which, plainly, she was the head. The room itself, which could not have been less than thirty by sixty feet, with windows on three sides, commanded a wide and striking prospect of nearly all the upper part of Manhattan Island as well as the East and North Rivers and the Jersey side of the bay. Interiorly it was crowded with benches like a schoolroom; some twenty or more desks, each with a typewriter attached. And at each desk an industrious, if not always attractive, typist. For the directress of this busy chamber, as I soon learned, did not view the comely typist of tradition with any too kindly an eye. She was not calculated, as she frankly said, to concentrate wholeheartedly on her task. And as I at once noticed, while her own large, square desk—a most pretentious affair—stood between two tall windows commanding the best of the views, those of her assistants faced her and the less interesting views.

On this occasion very little passed between us, as I recall, save conversation as to terms, which, incidentally, proved to be quite reasonable. She did add, however, that though legal work was the main body of her business, she liked to do "literary work," because even though there was little money in it for her, she was so interested in books and stories—yes, even articles such as mine. At once I was both interested and amused. To find any one moved to type anything I had thus far written for the pleasure of doing "something literary" was, as I saw it then, not a little naïve. My stuff literary! Indeed? In the face of indifferent or better, as yet, wholly unconscious editors and publishers, something to know. I went away asking—and could one obtain satisfaction from the writings of one who had no reputation, was not known?

Encountering my fellow-craftsman at dinner, I told of the find I had made—a typist who was not only pleasing physically and mentally, but from a practical point of view most inexpensive. And because of the large staff she employed, she would be able to return a manuscript typed within three or four hours, assuming that one left it before noon. More, she was impressed!

Now this recommendation so affected my friend that a day or two later, having a manuscript of his own to be typed, he announced that he was going to the same place. And, to my surprise, I did not see him again for several days. When he did return he stated that he had been with a friend whom he had not seen for a long time. I was surprised and dubious, but not pressing. Presently, not suffering any inquiries on my part, he began expatiating upon Miss Murtha. I was right. Not in a long time had he met any one more intelligent, generous, accommodating, the soul of efficiency and business skill. Had I talked with her much? I confessed I had not. Well, he had, and had discovered that she possessed a world of common sense as well as literary and artistic judgment. In his first interview with her, as he now explained, he had come to know her quite well. In short, and from the first, it was as though he had known her for years. Indeed, he had even visited and dined at her home—a most comfortable one in Jersey City, as he now explained, where *Rona,* as he already called her, dwelt with her mother, a maiden aunt, the girl who acted as her assistant manager at the office, and an old Irish cook who also functioned as general factotum. I was very much interested, but knowing his way where girls were concerned, not very much surprised.

But this was but the beginning of things. For there was a second disappearance of several days' duration, which, incidentally, brought to a standstill a bread-and-butter article we were jointly composing. Later, he returned to say that again he had been with Rona, or rather her family, yet only in the purest or most platonic sense, as I must most unhesitatingly as well as truthfully believe. For this, of course, was one of those rare and entirely platonic contacts wherein people immediately come to understand each other. Indeed owing to a profound psychologic as well as temperamental appreciation, the one of the other, as well as a wholly frank explanation on his part of his present economic and social or marital state, Rona had suggested that since he was quite without funds at present, he might just as well occupy a room in her home. There were several unoccupied. And certainly, as he put it, I saw nothing wrong in it. Was not art, art? And an artist a privileged as well as to be encouraged gift to the world? I thought so. Certainly therefore there was nothing essentially wrong in it. Kismet. Less poignant and less sensual than myself, he could undertake such relations, I was sure, without necessarily involving a climax.

But let that be as it will. The more immediate thing in so far as I was concerned was that he had already told her all about me—the essentials and peculiarities of my own erotic vagrom and at times altogether incalculable disposition, interests, relations. Also (he was sure) she understood them. And in addition all about *us*—the peculiarly harmonious and now altogether enmeshed psychology which caused us at first sight, as in the case of love between the sexes, to at once recognize each other for what we were and Damon and Pythias-wise, or what you will, to fall mentally and socially in step.

But I am beforehand with my tale, as I see. For there is that old brownstone house in Jersey City. It is still there. Years after all this I now tell had gone, I passed it once, of a summer evening. Strangers were sitting upon the old brown stoop in front, as once long before and of a summer evening, Winnie, Rona, her mother and aunt, and myself and my wife had sat, talking and dreaming. There were the same (as to design) brown awnings; the same open windows, open to the cool of the evening; and the voices of the various neighbors on their stoops. Only now a new Rona gazing adoringly, even slavishly, at a new Winnie, mayhap. Different minds, maybe, and dreams, but functioning in the same aspiring or despondent way. Ah, what is man, Sire, that thou art really mindful of him?

But, pardon, for I am still ahead of my story.

I was talking of this encounter! What a change for us, Winnie and myself I mean, from that day on! For, decidedly, this new contact with which he was so much taken was a blow of sorts to that very precious mental connection between Winnie and myself. For friendship, even as love, is that way, you know. "Thou shalt have no other gods before me." And certainly here was another god, or goddess. And this goddess, or its mother at least, had means—much more than any with whom Winnie had been previously identified. For while I had seen the large office and staff, spelling after a fashion, a quite comfortable income, he was now also reporting concerning the house in Jersey City as well as other houses and lands which this same mother of Rona as well as her aunt and another aunt somewhere else owned in the State of New Jersey and all of which were to come to this same Rona at the death of said relatives. And although, as I know, the said Rona was by no means anxious or waiting for her beloved and affectionate relatives to die, still she had confided all this, and to one who for all his philosophy and romanticizing was still not above houses and lands, assuming that they came to one without too much bother and did not affect one's literary dreams and plans. More,—by no means mercenary—for he created and gave always as much or more in joy or thought or aid than he received—still he was interested by this. And no doubt Rona was glad and hoped by way of material treasures as well as a very genuine adoration, as I came to know, to hold him. At least her subsequent actions will rather bear me out as to this, I think.

But hold! Do not despair. I am getting on.

At this time Winnie went on to explain, and in a somewhat wistful and disturbed fashion, as I thought, that our own happy relations were by no means to be disturbed, let alone disrupted, by this new connection. Ah no! By no means. By no means. For Rona already understood all. She really did. He had made it all perfectly plain how essential each was to the other. And, besides, was she not just too wise and considerate, as I would presently come to know, to wish to come between such a promising literary union? She was. Indeed, and truth to tell, she understood how perfect and helpful was this friendship between us. At best—and that was the thing which now among others he had returned to talk to me about—she wished only to share it, in the way that my wife shared it; to make a fourth; to be a help in any such way as she could.

For had she not means? And what, as she had already said to him, did she wish to do with those but be happy in some small way? Help, if she could, to make others happy. (I am thinking now of how really sincere she must have been; how unfortunately for her, at least, sincere.) We must all meet at her house, and soon—(a grand inaugural dinner it should be)—and go somewhere together afterward—a beach, a mountain resort. Also, there were in her house, and entirely apart from the room already occupied by Winnie, two rooms and a bath, with excellent furniture, now vacant. They had been occupied by her father, dead these many years. Obviously, this was the suite with which Winnie was being enticed. But now he pointed it out as something which was to be at our disposal also, and at any time—rooms, meals, service, all. This was a little too much for ordinary consumption, but did it not sound well? It did. Very generous, indeed.

None the less and to our general dissatisfaction, I fear, it resulted in little more than a series of conferences between my wife and myself, as to the meaning of it all. Should we or should we not accept these very generous overtures with anything but caution? To be sure, I had seen the lady. It was really because of my visit and comments that all this had come about. None the less, was it not Winnie and not us—not even me —in whom Rona was really interested? And while she was charming and generous and this and that— and her attitude and Winnie's, also, suggestive of many and delightful social contacts later, was it really not the better part of common sense to wait or go slow and allow this relationship to develop more temperately and casually? We thought so. For was there not, as yet, Winnie's wife and child figuring rather troublesomely in the background? And Winnie himself almost a trifle too light as even I thought at the time, in his apparent total and quite casual dismissal of the other relationship. And his wife's situation at the moment not exactly easy but difficult! I thought of that, too. Yet verily, here and now a most interesting and curious love match, which, as all love matches do, must prove more exclusive than inclusive; hence, best to be reticent, recessive, on guard against proving ourselves a nuisance. And so, as much of a genuine reserve as possible, only not so great a reserve as to prove wholly adequate against the persuasive influence and powers of Winnie. Indeed there was really no gainsaying him. A dinner engagement had to be accepted and after that a return dinner planned. Later there was a camping trip, followed by a joint week-end visit to one of the adjacent seaside resorts. For all this was during the summer following the spring in which I had encountered Rona.

But in the meantime, what a period of strenuous psychologizing on the part of all! For while Rona was charming as a person and generous to a fault where Winnie was concerned, still there was the usual difference of opinion that springs from or lies in the

vantageous or disadvantageous viewpoint of the ob-
server. For myself though I liked Rona well enough as
a clever, diplomatic and attractive person who was
naïvely interested in "literature" or "letters," or whatever might have been meant by her personal reaction
to those words. Most certainly I had not as yet seen her
as part and parcel of any broad and sensitive and colorful point of view such as that which distinguished
Winnie. On the other hand, he seemed either to see or
wish to see her almost wholly in this light. She was, as
he described her, all of these things, and more. On the
contrary, my wife, who certainly conceived of herself
as bringing a sensitive and poetic view to this earthly
picture, had instantly on meeting her decided that she
was something less, much less indeed than was included in Winnie's picture. As usual, as she said to
him and to me—yet with never anything much more
than a friendly and so mild trace of criticism—Winnie
was rhapsodizing. Rona was nice, surely; not beautiful by any means but attractive, and certainly
generous where he was concerned, but to us only on
account of him and not otherwise. I might depend on
that. For, despite all of Winnie's gay ravings about a
platonic friendship disturbed by nothing so human as
commonplace love or sex, and Rona's inclusive generosity which covered all of us—or would, and bordered
on extravagance and even folly—still, as my wife said,
Rona was concerned with Winnie—her love or infatuation for him, and so sex. My wife could tell, couldn't

she? Besides, there was that other angle to the situation. Winnie's wife and child? We'd better be careful, that's what!

And, in consequence, no living in the same house, ever. Just visits and now and again theater parties and what not else. But with constantly more than troubled thoughts on my part as to the outcome of all this. For try as I might, and in the face of all of Winnie's managerial optimism, (for that was about all that his raving came to), I could not feel that the thing was working satisfactorily. Was a man (myself, no less) to contest with a woman (Rona) for the possession of a second man's (Winnie's) affections? Yet, in another sense no contest or rivalry on my part. For I cared not at all how intimate, affectionately and sensually, Rona and Winnie might become, so long as the intellectual companionship which had distinguished our personal and literary relationship remained the same. But would it? Could it? From the first I observed consciousness on Rona's part of the strong and binding mental as well as emotional chemism which drew Winnie and me together—a union not likely to be even partially, let alone wholly, affected by any influence which her regard for him or his for her might bring to bear. He might do this or that for the time being—think he had gone from me forever, quarrel with me, even hate me a little for a time—but never, never would he cease to care. We both intuitively knew that and from the first. It was the thing that was never flatly picturized or characterized by either of us, yet was always present, as real as any floor or door; in short, the absolute thing out of which floors and doors are made and from which primarily they take their rise. And it was the jeopardy of this relationship which was now causing this thought and worry.

But because of my affection for Winnie, I let myself believe his many assurances. More, because of Rona's technical or commercial aid, henceforward to be furnished for next to nothing,—speedy and endless re-types, if need be,—we were to work faster and so accomplish more. Lastly and regardless of my doubts and reservations, in regard to Rona and Winnie's proffered hospitalities, there was constant entertainment chiefly at her place. For, as I found, hers was truly an agreeable home. Her father, as it appeared, had been a colonel in a New York Regiment during the Civil War—a dashing and captivating person; one who, as Rona told us, knew not a little about law and literature. His grandfather before him had been an officer in the American Rebellion. In fact, the whole place smacked of tradition and means. And Rona and her mother and aunt were really very presentable people, soft-spoken and self-effacing. True, the mother and aunt were, as Rona laughingly explained, profoundly immersed in the mysticism of the Catholic Church. But she was not. Rather, and like her father, she was, she said, the religious black sheep of the family. She had never been able to believe anything save that which appealed to her as reasonable. Worse, and which was why she was interested in Winnie, as she laughingly said, she had taken to books, realism, philosophy, art. Only for the sake of peace, she went to church at times. But with her eye, gayety, a good time. Her poor mother and aunt! And Father Doolcy, the parish priest! Already he had given her up as a bad job. And her chief value to her mother and aunt, as she also explained, was that she understood business and could manage their affairs, and so they were content to resign all to her.

But between Rona and myself, and for all these newer days which involved my working with Winnie at her home as well as he at ours, dinners, week-ends —most of which Rona insisted on paying for—what a battle! It was not that I wished it. Actually, if Winnie had been able to make a choice, it would have rested so without argument on my part. But there was everything to show that despite her sudden and strong affection for him and his desire to share her material and spiritual aid, he was still convinced that it was necessary for him to split his creative if not emotional life with me. And since I could not be with him in Jersey City, except for a meager portion of the time, he would come to me, and for days at a time when the work seemed pressing. And at such times, as far as I could gather, all he would do would be to leave a note, or after his departure call her up at her office and explain. At other times, being at her place, we two might lock ourselves in and the task being sharp refuse to desist until long after she had arrived. Sometimes, as was quite obvious from telephone conversations between them, she resented this. Sometimes she would try staying away a day or two herself, but would invariably capitulate and either wire or send a messenger with a note asking if she could not come up, or if we would not join her for dinner. And sometimes, to save her face, she would pretend that pressure of work necessitated her presence at the office late when well she knew she was making it possible for Winnie to depart without resort to subterfuge or indifference. And this she did with a gay smile.

Yet all the while, Winnie's interest in Rona, as I had witnessed from the first, was a divided thing; half, or more, practical; the remainder a genial, platonic liking that could not be too much strained. For he was never highly sexed. Indeed in his interest in her and what she represented was actually included in so far as I could see what that same might mean to us,—himself and me—(our joint relationship as struggling writers) in the way of pleasures and comforts. And so, for that reason as much as any, wishing to retain it. Intellectually, I am sure he was convinced that Rona was neither his nor my mental or emotional equal—merely one who gathered a sense of some of the phases of him—and who was haunted by a mad desire to be above all things made into something—anything—which he might choose to make of her as long as it was his ideal. Her greatest value to him, as

I saw, and knew that she knew also, lay in her money and her sensible and practical use of the same in his behalf.

On the other hand—and with what pangs I have often wondered!—he must have considered the spareness of the prospect for himself and myself alone—apart, that is, from Rona. For personally and with how little profit I was busy with a type of thing that was not destined to sell soon. Not only that, but in so far as our joint work was concerned I was inclined to drive, whereas Winnie, and especially now, was drawn to a more leisurely pace. Why not? Rona had means. She was constantly talking of and urging all toward this and that leisurely thing—week-ends or vacations at the sea or in the mountains; amusing trips for Winnie and us even though at times she could join us but for a part of the time. What difference—be it summer or fall! Why not gather pleasure, while we might.

Yet even so, I then felt, and still feel, that Rona was amply repaid by even the partial presence and affable gayety of so charming a dreamer and poet. For where could she have found his like—the joy of being near him, hearing him talk, seeing him smile. Or when? Ah, the beauty of his head, as she once exclaimed in my presence! The water-blue clearness of his eyes! The cherub-like pinkness of his cheeks and lips! And for all these, his profound philosophic cogitations and his optimism, which later would have done credit to Plato himself, and with which he could dissolve one's darkest moods. Veritably, a hypnotist that youth—one who by reason of the melody of his voice, the color and music of his fancy, incantated and lulled to dreams, to impossibilities and difficulties, really. Tragedies also. For surely, surely, as in the case of Shelley himself, his gay path lay among tragedies—for others.

I recall now, and with honest sympathy, Rona's troubled attempts to make the best of the situation. For quite all her efforts at that time and later seemed bent on seducing him with the prospect of perpetual comfort and even luxury. She was even determined now to do something for his wife and child, thus seeking, as I saw it, to bind Winnie to her in that way. So presently a proposal and a very liberal one. Why should he not let her bring the child on and send her to school; assist his wife with a small allowance maybe— two propositions which when first made were most promptly rejected, although later, if I recall aright, accepted—at any rate, some aid given. Again, as I soon noted, he was now wearing new suits, new shoes, and a new hat, and all far better than any I had previously seen him indulge in. I drew my own conclusions.

However, having lapsed into this situation and being now confronted by this new dilemma, and having neither the wish nor the will to interrupt either of these relationships, Winnie was put to it to think of some device for keeping us all together. And this, as the first winter passed and a second spring drew near, he eventually found. For there were, as he one day suddenly announced—and with that gay air of finality which so brightly colored so many of his announcements or suggestions—so many places by the sea or in the mountains not far from New York where, did the four of us but choose—(only Rona being so busy here could not participate much) all might go presently and enjoy such wondrous delights the while we worked and worked as before. Only, as I now most ruefully recalled, we had not, since Rona arrived, done as much work as before. Worse, Rona, as usual, was prepared to pay for it all and that was a little too much. For myself I refused at once. But then there was himself and Rona still to deal with. They had talked it all over. It was all so simple. She was either going to rent or build a cabin somewhere. And could I refuse that? Verily both of us were dreaming of doing each a novel at the time. And where, under what more ideal conditions could we be united in work? The proposition was really too ideal to reject especially when he and Rona so much desired it. Ruefully I scratched my head. For how often had I longed for a place by the sea. And now,—well, whisper to a starveling of Grub Street of the mountains or the sea in summer, and note how difficult it is to extract a negative. The thing had an enormous romantic appeal.

Worse, early in the ensuing spring, he announced to me that he and Rona had at last found an island off the coast of Connecticut, at or near the east end of

Fisher's Island. The truth was, of course, that Rona, through her own efforts, yet at his instigation, had found this small island belonging to a millionaire cotton manufacturer and had leased it for a period of years. Also he and Rona, as he now stated, had already arranged with a local contractor to build a small cabin, the details of which he there and then submitted to me for approval. And another day, only some weeks later, he came to tell me that the place was actually ready and that he and I were to go and occupy it. Rona could come up only every second or third Saturday at most for a week-end. For the rest of the time we were to have it all to ourselves. And how beautiful I would find it to be! A heaven! A paradise! Ah, wait! We could loaf, sail, work, dream, lie in a hammock, or sit in a comfortable chair and watch a world of sea traffic go by. Heigh ho, the gulls! The little sailboats! Ah, the cool breezes! The wonderful views! How could I think of not coming to such a place?

None the less, I was dubious. And the base of my criticism was that all of this smacked of parasitism. How could he, I, my wife, so freely accept of this and that and make no adequate, or even inadequate, return? And not only that but Rona did not like me, and he as well as I knew it. How could she when I was really rivaling her in his affections? More, had she not really prepared this place for him and her? It would never end right. Nevertheless, he insisted that I was all wrong. Rona did like me well enough. It was only of himself and his interest in me that she was jealous. But that would wear off. Time would smooth out all wrinkles. She would come to understand how necessary we were to each other in our work. We must be more diplomatic. He would be, and I would be.

Accordingly, all things being arranged and Rona not being able to come for three weeks, or my wife either (a trip west debarring her), I finally journeyed to this place and found a veritable dreamland, —blue sea, gulls, sails, ships, the comforts and luxuries of a little island cabin, such as wicker chairs; a wooden swing on the rocks outside; a rowboat; a fourteen-foot "sharpie"; and a lovely sandy beach on the lee or still side of the island where one could bathe. And on the other the great Sound steamers and all Sound shipping passing within a mile or two of our door.

The days and nights when in wind and storm the waves gnawed fiercely at the rocks, pounded and thundered below our very window. The misty, foggy nights, when as in a shroud this lone, small island lay severed from the world. One could hear only the mourning bells of guide ships, the eerie horns of lighthouses—Race Rock, Fisher's Island Light, Gull Island, Watch Hill. And yet at sunrise or sunset or noon of a fair day, how glorious the sea! The waters once more dancing and gurgling in the light—the winds lightly fingering the waves or one's cheeks or hair; the clouds floating like lighter boats upon a more diaphanous sea. Only about the rocks about which the wavelets now played, a spar or prow or steering wheel of some small vessel, broken by the storm. And once, upon the very rocks below my window, the whole of a pilot's cabin, with the name of the vessel printed plain—The Jessie Hale.

But never at any time any cessation of the suggestion that the sea was the dangerous, deadly, deceiving thing that it was. Calm it might be as any inland pool, yet but a brief half hour after and behold a thrashing and overcast world—dark rain clouds, fog, rain, hail, gigantic leaping billows that thwacked the rocks of this petty continent with mighty thwacks, flung spume and salt to the very windows. Sometimes I wondered whether, were it not for brush and bowlder or a small windblown tree to which one might cling, might not one be blown completely to sea? The house itself fortunately was firmly tethered by wire. But even so, these high winds and thrashing waves, especially at night, gave one a sharp sense of insecurity. As for Winnie, he seemed to take it all calmly and even joyously and sang of the Isles of Greece and the early adventurings of men.

Wonderful as it was, though, I could never say that I was wholly happy here, not even at peace at any time, with myself, however much I might be with Winnie or the sea. For where was the true owner of this? In her office in New York, no less, or in her hot

home in Jersey City. And why was I here? Because
Winnie—and not she—wished it. Because he wished
to work with me and was satisfied that I wished to
work with him though she paid. It was all very trying! And the thought waves that then sped from New
York to me there. I could feel them! Yet when I talked
of all this to Winnie, or sought to, he waved me aside.
How little really I knew of Rona; her warm, generous,
self-sacrificing nature! Besides, it was so absolutely
true, as he and she had said, that her work at this time
prevented her from leaving the city.

None the less, there were times when he appeared to
be at work on long compositions which he despatched
to her. And later a day when some of the work we
set out to do being done, she as well as my wife was
urged to come. Only in Rona's case there appeared to
be a trace of diffidence, if you please. She could only
come the first time for a week-end, or so she said,
some business matters recalling her to the city. But a
week or ten days later, and based on the success of the
first venture which went off gayly enough, she came for
a visit of two weeks, which was ultimately lengthened
to three.

Only throughout this second visit a subtle something
on the part of all which seemed to suggest more than
achieve restraint, although restraint there was. And the
reason, as I meditated on it afterwards, an underlying
floor of falsehood or self-deception which affected each
and every relationship here and which could not pos-

592 A GALLERY OF WOMEN

sibly be adjusted, or altered even, because of temperamental differences as well as differences in objectives. Nevertheless, on the surface one might have imagined that here was as gay a group as might be. The bathing, fishing, boating, daydreaming that went on. The conversation, arguments, laughter; the preparation and clearing away of meals; the plans for going here and there; the mishaps and achievements. Perhaps a superficial flaw was a somewhat dubious, albeit pretentious, platonism between Winnie and Rona, which was intended to convey that no intimacies beyond those permissible between wholly affectionate friends were here afoot, nor would be until marriage had united them. Yet there were times when this seemed a rather thin veil behind which real intimacies were enjoyed.

Only what of it, I thought? I, for one, and this in spite of the jealousy that I knew Rona entertained toward me, was actually gladdened by the sight of them holding hands, or of him kissing her or smoothing her hair as her head lay between his knees. Yet, as I also noted, with a marked absence of that salt of desire and especially that intense avidity for exclusiveness which is the mark sterling of all true passion. No, it was not there. He did not enough wish to be alone with her. For whenever there was opportunity for his going off alone with her, it was most often his wish that we—more especially myself—accompany him. And for his sake, apparently she would insist too. Whereupon I would feel that she was being ill treated.

For why should he wish to include me? Why not give more of himself to her or discard her entirely? There was something a little cruel about it.

Perhaps this was why, here more than elsewhere, I found myself liking Rona. A little too insistent at times, as to this and that I thought; a little garish and anon conscious of her especial property and largess as contrasted with our lack of means. Yet what of that? There were times, of course, when I became annoyed by her too efficient or too businesslike manipulation of the various material difficulties of life. We were to do this and that. Take this and that. Was there some trip or spot which we were thinking of taking or visiting? Presto! She would call Laura Trench, that ever-present assistant who lived with her —a kind of female fidus Achates or mental shadow— and to her would issue such commands and instructions as forthwith would insure all that was desired. It would have been pleasanter, as I often thought, to do with less and be free. Yet ever present was her wish to be generous. More because of her knowledge and ability to plan ahead everything went most smoothly and agreeably. At her order to Laura out would come wicker hampers of food, silverware, cutlery, dishes, a coffee or tea outfit, and always in charge of the female above mentioned, whose only fault was that she was by no means an attractive companion or equal. Yet Rona's whole point of view and nature, as I often thought at the time, might well have been such—she was really of such a liberal, kindly turn —as to require the privilege of ministering to others after this fashion. Who was I to say? Therefore I could not help feeling sorry for her, at times. Actually, I could almost feel her wondering how it was that she had allowed herself to slip into this quite anomalous position. Who was I that I should so engage Winnie against her? Why did I not drop out and leave Winnie?

And had I been psychically free, I would have, sure enough, only I was not as yet, any more than she. And what detained me so long in this wretched position was that I knew, and how well, that Winnie needed me as much as I needed him or he her—even more. That I and not she was his mental salvation. I even fear that she knew that. Only for her as for me he was all light and color—real charm and gayety and so surcease from my darker temperament as perhaps also for hers. Yet to me these days she was always so outwardly kind. And Winnie ever the same, poetic, dreamful, colorful—a persuasion to beauty and thought. One could not be near him and not find oneself afloat upon a glorious sea of fancy. Indeed it was as though his soul, like a spirit on wings of fancy, hovered only over what was lovely, entrancing, and avoided or was blind to that which was dark and sad.

And yet, in spite of, or rather because of, all this, and in the face of his fine plans and promises in regard to work, he was for the most part intolerant of the mere idea of it here. What, work here and now? "Oh,

come, let's not hurry this thing too much. You can't
do your very best unless you're in the right mood
for it. Suppose we think about it a little longer. There
are some parts of this that we haven't worked out
in our minds yet." And with this he would sweep
away any fine force or resolution that up to that moment might have seized on him or me, and sub-
stitute therefor that *dolce far niente* that I might
truthfully say was the dominating mood of his life.
And presently, after some five weeks of life with
him here—those precious inutile weeks as I see them
now—I found that there was no getting him to work
continuously at anything any more. Rather he would
prefer to, and did, stretch himself on the sand or in a
hammock or on a rock in the shade, and muse and
dream over the lovely spectacle that the sea presented.
And I, for my part, contemplating him here, was wont
to conclude that nature or life, or something, should
have immunized him against the necessity for toil—
persuaded him to be satisfied with Rona alone, for instance.

On the other hand, though, when Rona was about,
I could not always feel so about him. For hers was a
nature that was by no means so enamored of beauty as
was his. On the contrary, it was beauty as represented
by him, I think, that she saw and felt and no other.
Most poignantly through him to her came felicity.
This day hast thou transported me into Paradise!
But how could he keep her there? Would she not

stumble and fall from its crystal battlements if he so much as let loose her hand? I was sure of it. Hence that hunger in her eyes; that dread, hopeless yearning toward him. I saw it all so clearly and what actually it must come to. And I think that vaguely she felt that I saw this and hated me for it. I, the snake in the garden. I, Mephistopheles, peering from behind the flowery and perfumed vines.

So after a time, a talk with Winnie in which I sought to impress upon him how unfair it all was. We were not working. Why should I not go my own way? But no—he would have none of it. Was I now going to desert him? Unkind! Unfair! Oh, Lord, I once exclaimed to myself, what a mixup! What a damned contrary interruption or conclusion to a lovely beginning of something!

And so I stayed, only to see a change in him in regard to Rona. He became, as I saw, more restless, dictatorial, less patient with her, and unhappy, or comparatively so. Once, when she was alone and as she thought unseen, I saw her crying. There was a question of sailing. Being in no way a good sailor, she often suggested that she would prefer to be on land. But did that rescue her from his demands? On the contrary, the wind might be rough, the waves slapping and tossing the small boat, but it would be on just such an occasion that he would relinquish his place at the tiller and request her to take the line and rudder. And with what painful results! For Rona, always interested in her personal appearance, her hair, scarf, skirt, hose, would stop to consider these, letting go, maybe, either tiller or guy line. Then about would go the boat, pitching or rolling helplessly, ourselves in imminent danger of being engulfed. And then Winnie's rage!

"Rona, you can't do that! What did I tell you? You mustn't let go of the tiller or the line either. This is no place for fixing your hair. Wait till we get on shore or until I take the tiller, can't you?"

And now, and to my surprise, his voice had the ring of the severe and exasperated instructor. No seeming interest in the pretty spectacle she presented.

I recall one summer's evening when we sailed over to Budge's Island, something over a mile or more away, using the fourteen-foot "sharpie," which was our only other conveyance apart from a rowboat. The leg-of-mutton sail was inclined to slip from its sockets and the rudder was not very soundly hung. The billows were racing and cresting, the boat's nose high in the wind. And Rona, as usual, had brought along her collection of toilet articles as well as her bag upon a golden chain about her waist. And this in the face of constant reproval on the part of Winnie, who asked how was she to sail if she was not going to leave such nonsensical things at home. The answer was that she was sorry, she would be careful, though. And careful she was for a time, the boat speeding past the rocks at the end of the island and out into the channel at a rate that made the blood tingle. High masses of clouds were scudding overhead.

Presently, some little conversation having sprung up, Rona was forgetting the sail. Something about her trinkets had taken her attention, and she was pulling too tight. The boat was leaving its course.

"Rona!" called Winnie, sharply. "Watch what you're doing!"

Shocked by this, instead of doing as directed she gave the sail a jerk, and the wind catching it behind threw the beam violently across our ducking heads. The rope was torn from her hands and we found ourselves washing sidewise over a cresting billow, a second one breaking over us. Fine, I thought—at this rate we shall all be in the water soon. Yet I felt sorry for her. And Rona felt sorry for herself, as any one could see. She had sought vigorously to cling to the rope, which was the one thing she should not have done. The sail now flapped straight before the prow and we were lurching and rolling. I, being forward of the others, leaned out and sought to recover it while Winnie took an oar and sculled about until the sail swung within my reach. And then, the guy rope once more in Winnie's hand, he turned his attention to her.

"You little fool!" he fairly hissed. "Are you ever going to learn to sail?"

Her cheeks flushed and her eyes brightened. "I wish you wouldn't talk to me like that," she replied. And then more softly but with considerable determination: "You sail." Her mental state was really pathetic.

"No!" insisted Winnie, his voice rising to a high pitch. "You'll either sail this boat correctly or you'll never go out with me again."

Heigh-ho, I thought—big words from a man who owns not a penny of all this, neither boat nor cabin nor island nor her either. But I looked aside, catching as I did the helpless glance in her eyes. And she bit her lips and resumed her work of trying to guide the boat. Only in doing so she first paused, as so often she had before—from sheer nervousness in this instance—to arrange her beloved trinkets in her lap so that they should be safe. And in so doing, again the guy line for a fraction of a second was drawn too tight, the rudder released. This so infuriated Winnie that he reached over and seizing her free arm which was still trying to assemble the trinkets, and snatching all of them—purse, rouge box, eyebrow pencil, a small pad with a gold pencil, some small gilt bottles—threw them all into the sea,—and without a protest from her.

And once ashore, she beat a hasty retreat, her face white. To his credit, after a time Winnie, as I could see, followed her and peace soon reigned. Her tears were dried, her smile as gay as ever. And later, at midnight, when, poetwise, he spread a pallet for himself out on one of the rocks, it was Rona who crept to him carrying a pretty silk coverlet. And there she lay near him, happy in part at least, you may be sure.

The same way with fishing. She would pretend that she liked to fish. Yet the flopping of the fish in the boat when caught, the necessity of baiting one's hook and extracting the same from the fish, which bloodied her hands, were all decidedly distasteful to her. In fact at times I used to marvel at the amount of open pretense she was willing to inject into this affair, her delight in being near him making up for all. But all told, the general atmosphere was becoming not only distasteful but painful. In it no longer was the beauty we had all come for.

So now, in the face of this new attitude on Winnie's part and Rona's pursuant misery, I decided to go. What was the use? I was not spiritually happy here. Neither was Winnie. Neither was Rona. And no work accomplished either. And so, in spite of his protests and hers, I trumped up an excuse and returned to New York.

Yet with what thoughts! For certainly Winnie, for the time being anyhow—his financial condition being what it was—would not leave Rona, however much he might resent her. And she, however much she might resent my presence on her own account or my going on his—his reactions in regard to her—would still do nothing unless some order or move of his compelled her so to do. In short, here was one of those amazing and literally anomalous situations which could be neither eased nor solved by even the wills, let alone the actions, of any or all of the individuals involved.

And so at last then the end of that. Winnie was soon
returning to New York, he said—both he and Rona.
And there were still all of those things we had agreed
to do together. And they must be done. Yet they were
never done. Rather I merely heard from him a few
times. Would I not return? He (and Rona) wished to
see me.

But I did not—went out of New York upon an as-
signment or so I said. Whereupon taking umbrage,
maybe—I am not sure—and resigning himself, I assume, to Rona, he ceased writing and I heard nothing
more until late the ensuing fall, when he appeared to
announce that he and Rona had married. He had
thought it all over and had decided that he should so
do. His wife—through Rona's aid, as I afterwards
learned, she having gone west to see her—had secured
a divorce. There had been a settlement—on Rona's part,
of course. Now they were living in the old family
home in Jersey City. And both he and Rona would be
glad to see me. (I could scarcely restrain a smile at
this.) And so far as I could gather, all was to be as
before between us. There were the novels we had
wanted to write together,—each his own but with the
other's encouragement. In addition, finances would not
bother him so much now. And, by the same token,
should I wish it, they need not bother me—at least for
the period of writing the novel, or so he hinted.

But being sensitive as to that and still dubious of
Rona and her feeling for me, I decided not. More, sev-

eral visits to the new home convinced me of the wisdom of this. For although outwardly she was as friendly and urgent as ever, still behind a gay, smiling face was the mood which said that if I returned it would not be well for her. Winnie might not care for her so much. Why did I have to come? Why was he so determined to include me, when here she was? I felt rather than saw this, but gave no sign. Instead I pretended to agree absolutely, thinking all the while how odd it was that this more or less indifferent mood on his part should at last have led to such sure social if not exactly mental cleavage between us. Never again were we likely to work together. She would not like that; would prefer that it did not occur.

Yet for some time thereafter, and just the same, there were various desultory attempts on the part of Winnie and myself to function as co-authors. Days when he came to my place or I went to his. But always, always, that same note of fear as well as opposition on her part. I was seeking to take him from her. I was the lone corruptive fly in this otherwise perfect marital ointment. Only it was worse than that, as she really knew. For it was not I but Winnie or Life itself. And how was she to adjust that? For, as I was beginning to see, his was a temperament, lovely as it might be in the brighter and more speculative aspects, which required some solidifying or driving energy to coalesce his various shifting moods into literary reality. Also, more and more as I worked with him, I was beginning to think that I could do better alone. He was, as I saw him now, too fanciful and too erratic. He could not and would not concentrate sufficiently. And since Rona would not like me now or ever, why bother? He had made a world of his own. Rona had solved all his material problems for him and he did not really need me. And finally, sensing my mood as to this, I think, he finally decided to go his way, for the time being anyhow.

Then months of silence. This colorful connection really over, as I thought,—never to be resumed, I even grieved concerning it. The good old days! All had been so idealistically valuable to me. Then chancing to meet in a street in New York one day that same young secretary and assistant manager to Rona who had been with us on various trips, I heard a story of changes in the spirit and business acumen and enthusiasm of her employer which interested me. True, Rona and Winnie were married. And this had proved a great satisfaction to Rona. She was very happy, even now, and would be, apparently, in the future, if only Winnie would behave himself. But here was the rub. He was too impractical and was constantly urging Rona to adventures which were in no way good for her. For instance, already and at a great expense, and in spite of her mother's opposition, she was remodeling the old home in Jersey City in order to provide Winnie with a suitable studio. Also, they were tired of the island—Rona had never really liked it up there—and there was now instead a mountain lodge in the Catskills to which they repaired from time to time. And in addition they were now planning to enlarge and improve the grounds about this place, because it was not exactly as Winnie wished it.

"But how was it," I asked now, "that Winnie and she decided to marry so suddenly? I thought it more of a happy friendship than anything else."

"Happy friendship indeed!" she returned, with a quite noticeable sigh. "Happy friendship for him, perhaps. But not her. She was always in love with him and now she is the most changed person I ever saw. I never would have believed that any one could change so. Any one as strong and self-reliant as Rona was. She is so crazy about him that he rules her as though she were his slave. There isn't a single thing that he wants that she won't give him if she can. She would sell her mother's home in Jersey City and move away from there if her mother would let her, because he doesn't like it over there."

"But . . . love . . . you know," I interjected.

"Yes, love, to be sure. It certainly is," she went on. "Why, she used to be down to the office early and stayed late, every day, but now since they are married, and whenever they are here, she never gets down before ten and is ready to leave whenever he calls her. It isn't for myself that I'm talking, for I can get work anywhere, but to-day if it weren't for me and some of the other girls who have been with her for a long time, I don't know how things would be by now. After you left the island, you know, she stayed there for nearly six weeks, with only just telegrams and me going up there Saturday and Sunday to talk things over. And now he's getting her to invest in real estate in Newark, because he thinks he knows something about that."

I could feel that this girl was nursing certain grievances which centered about Winnie's dictatorial treatment of her. But the picture that interested me most was the one that she painted of Rona's life, since Winnie had come into it. Once a girl who was nearly all business, tending strictly to the affairs of her office, now she was almost entirely taken up with literary matters. Since her marriage, she had even come to dislike her business which once was everything to her, wishing even that she was out of it so that she might devote herself entirely to books. Nightly now, according to Laura, she was engaged in either listening or reading to Winnie from nine until midnight or later. Or taking down his stories in shorthand—anything that he might wish to dictate, particularly chapters of the novel on which now, as she explained, he was still attempting to concentrate.

The thought of his working on that first novel and possibly completing it while I merely fumbled at mine! Ah!

Worse for Rona, as Laura further explained, certain larger blocks of her business which formerly had come to her because of her personal solicitations and which she had retained by reason of the personal care she had been willing to give them, were now being allowed to fall into the clutches of rival agencies. In short, her business was now not nearly as large as it had been. Only this summer several of the girls had had to be laid off or let out, and still she was going ahead, saying that Winnie's novel was the great thing now and that she could look after her business later.

I marveled.

But then nothing more of any import in connection with them until one late day of the following February, when Winnie himself appeared at my place with a portion of an uncompleted novel—about two-thirds, I should say. And saying that he had been hard at work all winter but as yet had not been able to complete it. Also, as he now frankly announced, (and for which simplicity and directness, lack of literary pretense, one could not help liking him), he feared that it lacked inspiration in parts. Would I read it? He would like my advice. Then finding that I also was still working on mine, he begged of me the privilege of looking at it. He would read it and give me his honest opinion. We might as well, and ought really, as he now phrased it, work together on these things. Why not? We had always been the best of friends. Yet recalling the feeling that presumably still existed on Rona's part in regard to my supposed influence over him, I hesitated and said so. And then he announced that while it might be useless ever to attempt to straighten out that tangle, (it was true that Rona was a little jealous of me and my interest for him and his for me), still why should we allow that to stand in our way? Did not our work come first?

At that moment, as always, I realized that I cared for him as much as ever, and always would. There was something here that transcended errors, moods, follies, either of our own or another's making. We could and should work together.

And so another effort, out of which at last came two novels, my first and his. But for the accomplishment of this secret meetings, daytime visits on his part to my place. Yet, and even now, as he sought to show, Rona was the kindliest and best-intentioned person in the world, actually dying to be of genuine literary assistance to him; imaginative as well as practical, yet in so far as his work was concerned, not sufficiently close to his mood. He was sorry but so it was. She could never really inspire him to those so necessary nuances and shadings which he must achieve. Yet so helpful in all minor ways, such as typing, transcribing dictation and the like. Besides, by now he was too affectionately grateful to her for all of the things she had done and was doing for him to ever let her lacks make any real difference. She was so generous, loving, sweet . . . Didn't I know how it was?

The following spring, though, because of new plans on his part, and before either completed book was pub-

lished, he was off to the mountain lodge, built for him
by Rona, some required improvements calling him.
And why should I not come up? And this in the face
of his knowing why. Only then, because of changing
financial and literary conditions, I was compelled to go
west and south. And more, later, because of the sup-
pression of my own work and the unfavorable editorial criticism that followed, I fell upon hard psychologic as well as material lines and for a period
was in no state to undertake any serious labor. Between whiles, Winnie, because of new connections,
drifted far away. For a time I heard from him not at all,
and in a semi-neurotic mood grieved over those older
and better days. Later, he having written and published
several additional books, I heard of Rona, as the wife of
a probably rising author, one who finding herself de-
meaned by the typewriting agency, had given it over
entirely. It had been resigned to Laura who sought to
retain Rona's interest by holding a few shares for her.

Also Rona and Winnie, having had so much artistic
success, had retired to their mountain home, for a
period at least. And Winnie was already working
on another book—three in swift succession. In the
meantime, as I often said to myself, what was I
doing? Drifting? A failure?

As to his books—the novel, I may say, was a fairly
interesting piece of realism, but as I saw it entirely out
of his vein, too exaggerated realistically to be im-
pressive. He could not see life as it was. Next was a

colorful, though to me who knew him, obviously romantic, report of himself as a farmer and country gentleman—a successful farmer and country gentleman, making some thirty or forty acres of mountain farming land pay. But too full of things which did not quite articulate; too many unintended suggestions of failure or error to make it quite ring true. I wondered as to that. The third was a romantic and somewhat exotic study of his home life in the city with Rona and her relatives, bringing in many details of which I knew, but too cheerfully appreciative and appraising to be of any real value. The one thing in all these books that interested me was a graceful and appreciative picture of Rona as a wife and literary and artistic as well as practical helpmate, which, I felt, must have pleased her. In all she was shown as kind, intelligent, forbearing, gentle, and helpful as a critic. All of which she may have been. But were they really happy, I wondered. I could not quite believe it. And yet I was ready to believe that her very large generosity might eventually have changed him toward her.

Later, in New York, though, after an absence of a year or more, I encountered first Rona and then Laura Trench. Rona, whom I saw first and but for a moment, was as healthful as ever in appearance, but seemed nervous and worried. She and Winnie, as she recited, were still in the mountains in the summer; in New York in the winter. Rarely did they revisit the island. But her dear mother had died; the house in Jersey City had been sold; her old aunt had gone to a distant cousin. She and Winnie were but now planning a trip through New England. But I must come and see them after they returned. She would tell Winnie and he would write and tell me when. Then she was gone. And all the while I had felt in her that same nervous and uncomfortable distrust of me that had characterized her from the first.

Then the following fall, but without any intermediate word from either Rona or Winnie, I came upon Laura again and at once possessed news of both. They had returned to their apartment in town. Central Park West, no less. Laura, on account of the business which Rona had resigned to her, was and had been in rather close touch with them. She it was who helped them get settled in their new place here as well as in the mountains and was still doing many things in connection with their life. But as a bearer of glad tidings, she was little more than a crape hanger.

Winnie as a gentleman farmer? Oh, my! Or Rona as a happy wife? Oh, what nonsense! Or, again, Winnie's temperament as an author! One should see—as well as hear! And Rona's tolerant and even humble endurance of him in that capacity!!! In short, according to Laura, Winnie was one of the worst of the genus gentleman farmer that it had ever been her lot to meet. If one could believe her—(a young woman who had never much liked him but who was devoted to Rona) —he was the "greenest" and at the same time the most zealous, persistent, domineering and dogmatic farmer that had ever set a silver-handled spade or a beveled-edge hoe to the soil. And yet, by reason of Rona's coddling of him, he had set out to make a paradise of his own which should pay and pay well. Only it never had. And the nonsense as well as domineering of Rona that went with it! Why, it was a wonder she wasn't sick or dead! For, in the first place, this farm or country estate, as you will, had to be put in the most expensive order, Rona paying the bills—tools, stock, sheds, this and that bought and placed on land which was not any too good and had cost too much originally. Next, the farmers, builders, tradesmen, one and all, finding that they had an economic dunce on their hands, had proceeded to tell and sell him nearly anything that came into their heads. A cottage that should not have cost more than two thousand at that time—with all of the materials of which it had been constructed to be found on the place—had cost seven. Implements which were useless to him because once he had them he was not interested to do the work they were intended for, or to supervise the work of others at the wages asked, had cost him a thousand or more—and a large sum for stock which he had bought and then had not troubled to care for.

Then there were men who worked or loafed for him. These, aided by other native workers, had dug him a well, a cellar, a spring house, built him a barn, a road, various fences, all of which were defective, and since he did not farm much, useless. His pigs and chickens had died of diseases, or been stolen. A cow had been chased by a dog and injured. He himself, in attempting to fell a tree, had cut it on the wrong side so that it had fallen and damaged one corner of the roof. And betimes, over a period of nearly four years, during which all this had happened, he had been attempting to write, only latterly (within the last year or two), he had been complaining that his farm duties interfered with his literary composition. And all this interspersed with trips to New York, the island, even once to a brother who had betaken himself to the apple country in Oregon and was developing orchards there and in connection with which Winnie was now developing an interest—and might even go out there, leaving the farm to fare as it might.

Ah, lucky Rona, I thought—at least you have someone who keeps you busy worrying and so diverts your attention from the futility of life itself!

Yet speaking for Rona, Laura was full of her troubles. For apart from all the above, it was plain by now that Winnie was insufferably bored with Rona and indirectly, if not directly, manifesting it in a thousand ways.

"If I didn't know how much she cares for him, I couldn't imagine her enduring it. Not Rona! She has always been too commanding herself."

Also, as Laura saw it, Winnie had compelled Rona to share all his enthusiasms as they passed from one thing to another—farming, dairying, chicken raising, truck gardening. Equally he had compelled her to share the responsibility for every failure by insisting on her agreeing with him in everything beforehand. And to prevent things from going to waste or ruin, she had been compelled to work, and work hard, looking after people and things in whom and which she was really not interested, but which, in view of his neglect, had to be looked after. And yet, if she ventured to say a word or utter a complaint, Winnie would fly into a rage or sink into a sulky and unresponsive mood, or leave and come to New York—which, as Laura saw it, tortured her most of all. The horror of losing him! It was ever present now.

For whisper! There was a literary woman in the same apartment building in New York, of whom Rona was jealous. She was an actress betimes and had written a book. And with this woman, who was no more attractive than Rona, Winnie liked to dance and go places. And once, and worst of all, Rona had found a letter which Winnie had written me and forgotten to mail, in which he referred to a meeting with me and work and about which she had never heard before. And that had made her bluer and darker than nearly anything else.

"Believe it or not," she added, "the blackest thing in her life is you. For she still thinks that you influence Winnie against her in some way. I am sure she feels that if you had never been in his life, he would have cared for her more. You never liked her, she says, and you have made him feel that she isn't worthy of him."

I threw up my hands, for, as I have shown, I had no more intentional control over Winnie than I had over Sirius or Beltair. And now no longer any desire for such control. That was all dead. Besides, as I explained in the hope that it might come to Rona, was it not he who last had sought me out? True enough, Laura admitted, but since Winnie was becoming restless again and I was once more in the city, she was becoming fearful of my influence. For, as Laura said, he talked of writing another book and Rona feared he might return to me or possibly depart with the young actress.

By then, though, I was really weary of Winnie and his antics and intensely sorry for Rona, and I then and there determined not to see him again. And I did not for several years. But in the meantime, as I was eventually able to gather from various sources (Laura; Winnie's own brother, Donald, a successful organizer of an apple growers' association in the northwest; as well as several friends who knew both Winnie and Rona), that a third, and as it eventually proved, final, stage of this relationship had now set in. For it appeared later that just at the time when Winnie was becoming dissatisfied with his farm experiences as well as his literary unproductiveness and Rona, this brother of his had appeared on the scene with an interesting suggestion. What was Winnie really doing, he asked? Nothing! And yet, as he had long observed, Winnie had always possessed a most amazing faculty for persuading or cajoling other people to his way of thinking. Accordingly, why should he not enter upon this orchard formation labor with his brother? Be a great financial promoter? (A thing that must have fired Winnie's fancy.) Why not help to dispose of an immense tract in Oregon? Be a magnate? An apple magnate. There were millions in it!

And true to his temperament, Winnie was at once seized with the glory as well as the possibilities of this. Or, perhaps in it he saw a door to freedom—a different and more refreshing life. At any rate, another change for himself and Rona, as it proved. For now and at once, Winnie decided on her usefulness in connection with this adventure. She was to execute his financial dreams for him. And, Rona, as I was quite able to guess for myself at the time, was quite ready and anxious to fall in with this. For would it not take Winnie from New York and so possibly all the ills that were there threatening her? It did. Hence a swift removal to Oregon, followed by the building of a bungalow and the introduction of a car for their joint commercial and pleasure use, the developing and selling of these tracts requiring not a little transportation.

But, as I heard still later in connection with all this, Rona, not so much Winnie, proved a real success. In short, some years later, it was Winnie's brother Donald who told me that from the first she it was who displayed exceedingly keen judgment as to tracts, methods of development and sale, and the technical conduct of the business. Only there were certain persons back east whom it was still necessary to persuade to invest, and it was in connection with these that Winnie was to be used. For "persuasion," as his brother once said to me, was his other name. And this it was that troubled Rona most, since now and frequently it was necessary for him to return to New York in order to dispose of certain tracts, while she must remain in the west. As a result, a new phase of the old misery. For back in New York was there not that literary woman? And all the other temptations of the great city? And their apartment in which Winnie lived while there?

The truth was, of course, that love, if it ever existed, was dead. Or, at any rate, the influence exerted by Rona's means which had so enticed the stripling without a dime. More, Winnie was now in touch with individuals of considerable means in New York, as I found and knew, for I ran into him once, in connection with a group which centered about Glen Cove and Oyster Bay. Among them was much money, as represented by brokers, bankers and social idlers. Still more, as I soon gathered and even saw for myself, since I was out and around in those days, he was already in tow to a young and delightful widow of means who had just discovered him and thought him "marvelous," as indeed in many ways he was— especially when and where fortune appeared to be

favoring him. At once, on reëncountering me, he outlined this new great venture of his. It was this, that,—a
sure road to fortune. Would I not make one with him?
All I needed was money—which I did not know how
to get. But how was Rona, I asked. Oh, Rona,—
Oh, as fine as silk. Couldn't be better. Enormously interested in this new great thing, heart and soul. Had
dropped all to go out there and further it, and when
Rona was enticed by the practical side of anything, well,
I knew Rona. . . . (Yes, I knew Rona. And Winnie.)
And regardless of whether I had made a strike yet or
not—as I hadn't—he would gladly let me in on the
ground floor, set over ten or fifteen acres, if I would,
and carry me as long as possible without charges, or
so few that the thing would be easy, since soon these
things would take care of themselves. But remembering Rona and her feeling toward me, I declined.

But the widow. She was so young, brisk, witty and
attractive and good-natured. Poor Rona, I thought.
Your life line runs in rough places. This woman, or
girl, unless I am a poor judge of powers and capacities, will rob you of Winnie and keep him, for she has
a charm which is greater than yours—more means, a
fixed social position, and entry to a group which Winnie will be only too happy to join. In fact, never did I
see him more at home than upon the verandas and
lawns of various Long Island homes to which, in quest
of introductions and possibilities, he was escorted by his

new-found favorite. As a matter of fact, I was a small part of this myself during that particular summer.

But here is the rest of the story as it was eventually told me by Winnie's brother. By then it appeared that neither Winnie nor Rona were in any way any longer connected with the Oregon development. Rather, owing to the young and charming widow, Winnie had long since deserted Rona, who had eventually granted him a divorce, and now he and the fair widow were living at Glen Cove at times, in New York or London at others. Only, as I now learned, this brother and Winnie had had not a few arguments in regard to all this. As a matter of fact, after Winnie had gone it was Donald's intention to come to New York and see Winnie and, if possible, patch things up, for, as he stated, Rona's condition at the time was dreadful. She was all but destroyed. Only, as he soon found, the lady was extraordinarily beautiful and attractive. And besides, as Donald rather sadly argued, Winnie was not to blame, perhaps. He was enormously interested in and easily attracted by women, or rather a really clever woman, and he couldn't be shot for that, could he? Besides, Rona, as much as he admired and sympathized with her, was never the woman to hold Winnie. She was clever and practical but without any social flair, and she had found Winnie when he was much younger and when what she had had meant a great deal more to him than it possibly could to-day. As in the case of women, Winnie had always been curious about money and what it could do for him. But as sure as God made little green apples, he was not nearly as much interested in money as he was in women. And perhaps what interested him in a clever woman with money—since he had no talent for making or keeping money—was what that money would do for him *and the woman he was interested in*—the freedom it would give both to go, do, be, so long as they were together, not otherwise. And when he left it was not money he took or wanted, but the freedom to better and make gayer his life and that of some other woman, the woman who chanced to fascinate him mentally at the time.

But now as to Rona, please! What about her?

Oh, yes, Rona. Poor Rona! To be sure, a sad case that. A very sad case. For she was essentially or at heart a woman with conventional if not exactly moral ideas and one who looked upon love if not marriage as sacred. Being of Irish extraction, she was a good battler for what she thought was hers, or at least what she thought her capacities and fate should entitle her to. By the same token, a poor loser. Oh, yes, indeed, the Irish were that way sometimes. Worse, she was inordinately fond of Winnie, madly in love with him. Now, as he looked back on it, it was a wonder she had not taken her life at the time. And one day he thought she had. But that would come up a little later.

At any rate, I recalled, didn't I, the time when Winnie had come east and met this Mrs.—let us call her

Angel. I must, because it was shortly after that Winnie wrote him that he had come up with me again. Well, at any rate, it was after that Winnie began to display a desire to stay on in New York. At once Rona became morose and dour, and Winnie at her request came back to Oregon for a little time. But soon asked to be returned to New York, since he had succeeded in interesting a number of people there and was selling not a few tracts. Besides, for a time at least, Rona had been pleased by his financial achievements. But having heard of or suspected the presence of Mrs. Angel, she was set on Winnie's return to Oregon. Or if not she would drop her very valuable work and go to him—a proposition which somehow conflicted with certain obligations which she, apart from Winnie, had undertaken in order to secure certain rights and privileges in the new organization for herself and Winnie. This brought about Winnie's return for a time.

But then, of course, arguments and quarrels. There was some question once of a missing letter which came to the office instead of his home—and was, so Donald thought, from Mrs. Angel. It might as well have been from the devil, he said. The quarrel concerning it lasted a month, Rona not appearing at the office at all and Winnie showing every evidence of distress and absent-mindedness. He appeared almost incapable of any kind of work, and announced that Rona was in a bad way temperamentally, yet never explained how or why. Then one day he packed a bag and apparently regardless of Rona departed for New York, whereupon she followed. There was then a partial or temporary adjustment of some kind, by reason of which both returned to Oregon and dwelt for a few months together in the apple region. And Winnie went to work in connection with a San Francisco group.

But this was of short duration also. No go, as we say. Instead of returning at a certain time from San Francisco to Oregon he had gone direct to New York, dispatching from there a letter to Rona which seemed finally to convince her that do what she would she could no longer hold him, and so finally blowing up this western life. At the same time, Donald also received a letter from Winnie in which he confessed that he was in love, no longer interested in Rona, and while he might and would be willing to represent the corporation in New York, he would not return west nor would he again live with Rona. It was no use. Both were unhappy. Long before ever meeting Mrs. Angel, he had wished to be free, but being sorry for Rona and grateful for all she had done for him, had hung on. But now he was through. . . . He was sorry. Perhaps Rona would give him a divorce. It would be senseless for her not to. If not, then Reno. But, in the end, as Donald explained, Rona eventually acquiesced to divorce, after some six months of silence.

But in the end, what a dissipation of a dream, on Rona's part at least! For after Winnie's disappearance and the arrival of the aforesaid letter, a complete emo-

tional if not physical or mental break on her part.
She had been, as Donald said, in better spirits and
working more industriously than ever after their temporary visit to New York and subsequent reunion. But
then the letter, unknown of at first by Donald, followed by the sudden and unexplained abandonment
on her part of her office and duties. No word to
even her stenographers, who reported to Donald for
instructions. And so a call on his part at her house. But
no sound within. Until Winnie's letter he had
even decided that she had gone to San Francisco.
Afterwards to New York. But the local ticket agent
seemed to think not. And her car was still in the
garage.

Then after a week, a telephone call from her from
the house. She had been there all the time. But ill. And
would he come down? He went, only to look upon
some one who he said had the appearance of wax.
Yes, Winnie was gone. All was over between them.
She knew that now and was not going to try any
more. Rather, now, it was her single desire to be
relieved of all further work in connection with this
venture. Her shares and the house and all connected
with it, she wanted sold. She was going away and
would not say where she was going. A local bank
would take care of whatever matters the sale of her
interests might develop. And thereafter—something
over a week, if I recall him aright—she once more
shut herself in her bungalow without further com-

munication with him or any one, until one day she was
seen suddenly to depart.

But before all this, one illuminating, pathetic point.
On the third or fourth day of her second silence,
Donald said, having gone to her door one evening and
repeatedly knocked without receiving an answer, he
stood for a time meditating. And as he did so, so he
said, there came to him, first quite softly, later more and
more audibly, the sound of footsteps in a room on the
second floor—Rona's and Winnie's bedroom, as he assumed. It held Winnie's books, desk, papers, trunks.
And there she was walking for hours, he said, her steps
quite audible to him from where he stood. To and fro!
To and fro! Across the length or breadth of the old
room!

"Those steps!" he commented, quite emphatically. "I
never knew before how mournful and how meaningful
a walk might be. They were like the footfalls of a
ghost. For a long time after that I could scarcely bring
myself to forgive Winnie, although I well know how
little any of us are responsible for the temperaments
which drive us to do as we do."

But now as to Winnie once more. I met him and
his new wife from time to time in one smart quarter and another. And for a period of years at least he
was as gay and optimistic as ever. Later, something else
again,—but let that be. At last, as he then said, he had
the right conditions. And we might do this and that.
Write plays, for instance. I smiled to myself, although

I knew one book he could have written. A minor part of it is here.

As for Rona. Once, fully three years after Winnie had left her, I learned from Donald that he had heard that she had taken refuge in a certain theosophic retreat in Southern California, where those very much battered by life and in need of solitude, mental as well as physical, sometimes seek escape from the world and its ills. (The Roman Catholic influence, you see.) Later, as many as seven years, chancing to look one day into a classified New York directory and under "Stenographers and Typists" for a given name, I came upon the following, the address that of a well-known office building in the Wall Street neighborhood:

MRS WINFIELD VLASTO
Court Proceedings
Law Stenography—Conventions
Commercial Typing
Mimeographing, Multigraphing

I could scarcely believe my eyes, or my deductions. And yet never after had I the heart to investigate.

But why not? Was it not the thing she had really liked to do?

But after ten years!

And with what memories!

IDA HAUCHAWOUT

Ida Hauchawout

SHE is identified in my mind, and always will be somehow, with the rural setting in which I first saw her, a land, as it were, of milk and honey. When I think of her and the dreary, commonplace, brown farmhouse, in a doorway of which I first saw her framed, and later of the wee but cleanly cabin in which at last I saw her lying at rest, I think of smooth green hills that rise in noble billows, of valleys so wide and deep that they could hold a thousand cottage farms, of trees globe-like from being left unharried by the winds, of cattle red and black and white, great herds dotting the hills, and of barns so huge that they looked more like great hangars for flying machines than storehouses for hay and grain. Yes, everywhere was plenty, rich fields of wheat and corn and rye and oats, with here and there specializing farmers who grew only tomatoes or corn or peas or ran dairies, men who somehow seemed to grow richer than the others.

And then I think of "Fred" Hauchawout, her father, a man who evidently so styled himself, for the name was painted in big black letters over the huge door of his great red barn. This Hauchawout was a rude, crude, bear-like soul, stocky, high booted, sandy-haired, gray-eyed and red-skinned, with as inhospitable a look as one might well conjure. Worse, he was clad always, on Sundays and every other day, so I heard, in brown overalls and jumper. In short, he was one of those dreadful tramping, laboring grubs who gather and gather and gather, sparing no least grain for pleasure by the way, and having so done, die and leave it all to children who have been alienated in youth and care no least whit whether their forebear is alive or dead, nor for anything save the goods which he has been able to amass. But in this latter sense Hauchawout was no huge success either. He was too limited in his ideas to do more than hide or reinvest in land or cattle or bank his moderate earnings at a low rate of interest. He was quoted locally as living up to his assertion that "no enimel gets fet py me," and he was known far and wide for having the thinnest and boniest and hardest-worked horses and cows in the neighborhood, from which he extracted the last ounce of labor and the last gill of milk.

He was the father of three sons and two daughters, so I was told, all of whom must have hated him; those I knew did, anyhow. One of the sons, when first I wandered into the region, had already gone to the far west, after pausing to throw a pitch-fork at his father and telling him to go to hell, or so the story went. Another, whom I knew quite well, being a neighbor of a relative of mine, had married after being "turned out," as he said, by "the old man" because he wouldn't work hard enough. And yet he was a good enough worker to take over and pay for, in seven years, a farm of forty acres of fertile land, also eventually to acquire an automobile, a contraption which his father denounced as a "loafer's buggy."

The third son, Samuel, had also left his father because of a quarrel over his very human desire to marry and make his own way. Latterly, because he was greedy like his father and hoped to obtain an undue share of the estate at his death, or so his relatives said, he had made friends with his father and thereafter exchanged such greetings and visits as two such peculiar souls might enjoy. They were always fighting, the second son told me, being friendly one month and not the next, moods and different interests dictating their volatile and varying approaches and recessions.

In addition, though, there were two daughters: Effie, a woman of twenty-nine or thirty, who at the age of twenty-one had run away to a nearby large city and found work in a laundry and had never returned, since her father would not let her have a beau; and finally Ida, the subject of this sketch, whom I first saw when she was twenty-eight and who already showed the care and disappointment with which apparently her life had been freighted. For, besides being hard on "enimels," Hauchawout was hard on human beings and seemed to look upon them as mere machines like himself. It was said that he was up at dawn or earlier, with the first crow of the roosters, and the last to go to bed at night. Henry Hauchawout, the son I knew best, once confessed to me that his father would "swear like hell" if all his children were not up within five minutes after he was. His wife, a worn and abused woman, had died at forty-three, and he had never married again, but not from loyalty. Did he not have Ida? He had no religion, of course, none other than the need of minding your own business and getting as much money as possible to bury away somewhere. And yet his children seemed not so hard; rather sentimental and human—reactions, no doubt, from the grinding atmosphere from which they had managed finally to extricate themselves.

But it is of Ida that I wish to speak—Ida, whom I first saw when my previously mentioned relative suggested that I go with him to find out if Hauchawout had any hay to sell. "You'll meet a character well worth the skill of any portrayer of fact," he added. It was Ida, however, who came to the door in answer to a loud "Hallo!" and I saw a woman prematurely old or overworked, drab and yet robust, a huge creature with small and rather nervous eyes, red sunburned face and hands, a small nose, and faded red hair done into a careless knot at the back of her head. At the request of my "in-law" to know where her father was, she pointed to the barn. "He just went out to feed the pigs," she added. We swung through a narrow gate and followed a well-fenced road to the barn, where just outside a great pen containing perhaps thirty pigs stood Hauchawout, a pail in each hand, his brown overalls stuck in his boots, gazing reflectively at his grunting property.

"Nice pigs, eh, Mr. Hauchawout?" commented my relative.

"Yes," he answered, with a marked accent, at the same time turning a quizzical and none too kindly eye upon me. "It's about time they go now. What they eat from now on makes me no money."

I glanced amusedly at my relative, but he was gazing politely at his host. "Any hay for sale, Mr. Hauchawout?"

"How much you t'ink you pay?" he asked, cannily.

"Oh, whatever the market price is. Seventeen dollars, I hear."

"Not py me. What I got I keep at dat price. Hay vill be vorth yust five tollars more if dis vedder keeps up." He surveyed the dry green-blue landscape, untouched by rains for these several weeks past.

My relative smiled. "Very well. You're quite right, if you think it's going to stay dry. You wouldn't take eighteen a ton, I suppose?"

"No, nor twenty. I t'ink hay goes to twenty-two before October. Anyhow, vot I got I can use next vinter if I can't sell him."

I stared at this crude, vigorous, self-protective soul. His house and barn seemed to confirm all I had heard. The house was small, yellow, porchless, inhospitable, and the walks at the front and side worn and flowerless. A thin dog and some chickens were in the shade of one fair-sized tree that graced a corner. Several horses were browsing in the barn lot, for it was Sunday and the sectarian atmosphere of this region rather enforced a strict observance of the day. They were as thin as even moderate health would permit. But Hauchawout, standing vigorous and ruddy before his large, newly painted barn, showed where his heart was. There was no flaw in that structure. It was a fine big barn and held all the other things he so much treasured.

But it was about his daughter that my relative chose to speak as we drove away.

"There's a woman whose life has been ruined by that old razorback," he reflected after volunteering various other details. "She's no beauty, and her chances were never very good, but he would never let any one come near her, and now it's too late, I suppose. I often wonder why she hasn't run away, like her sister, also how she passes her time there with him. Just working all the time, I suppose. I doubt if he ever buys a newspaper. There was a story going the rounds here a few years ago about her and a farm-hand who worked for Hauchawout. Hauchawout caught him tapping at her shutter at two in the morning and beat him up with a hoe-handle. Whether there was anything between them or not no one knows. Anyway, she's been here ever since, and I doubt if anybody courts her now."

. . . .

I neither saw nor heard of this family for a period of five years, during which time I worked in other places. Then one summer, returning for a vacation, I learned that "the old man" had died and the property had been divided by law, no will having been left by him. The lorn Ida, after a service of thirty-two or three years in her father's behalf, cooking, sweeping, washing, ironing, feeding the animals, and helping her father to reap and pitch hay, had secured an equal fifth with the others, no more, a total of fifteen acres of land and two thousand dollars in cash. The land had already been leased on shares to her prosperous brother, the one with the automobile, and the cash placed out at interest. To eke out an existence, which was still apparently not much improved, Ida had gone to work, first as a laundress in a South Bixley (the county seat) laundry, at a later date as a canner of tomatoes in the summer canning season, and then as housekeeper in a well-to-do canner's family. She was reported by my host's wife as still husbandless, even loverless, though there was a rumor to the effect that now that she had property and money in the bank, she was being "set up to" by one Arlo Wilkens, a garrulous ne'er-do-well barber of Shrivertown, a drunken roistering, but now rather exploded and *passé* person of fifty; also one Henry Widdle, another ne'er-do-well of a somewhat more savory character, since he was credited with having neither the strength nor courage to be drunken or roistering. He was the son of a local farmer who himself owned

no land and worked that of others. With no education
of any description, this son had wandered off some
years before, trying here and there to sell trees for a
nursery and failing utterly, as he himself told me, and
then going to work in a furniture factory in Chicago,
which was too hard for him; and later wandering as
far west as Colorado, where necessity compelled him to
become a railroad hand for a time. ("I served my time
on the Denver & Rio Grande," he used to say.) But
finding this too hard also, he had quit, and returned to
the comparative ease of his former life here, which had
no doubt brightened by contrast. Once here again, he
found life none too easy, but at the time I knew him
he was earning a living by driving for a local contractor, that being "the easiest thing he could find," as
a son of the relative aforementioned most unchari-
tably remarked.

While working in this region again for a summer
under some trees that crowned a hill and close by a
highroad which crossed one slope of it, I was often
made aware of this swain by the squeak of the wheels
of his wagon as he hauled his loads of stone or sand
or lumber in one direction or another. And later I
came to know him, he being well known, as are most
country people the one to the other in a region such as
this. Occasionally as the two sons of my host worked
in a field of potatoes alongside the hill on which
I worked, I could see them hailing this man as he
passed, he for some reason appealing to them as a

source of idle amusement or entertainment. Hearing laughter once I ambled over and joined the group, the possibility of countryside news enticing me. He proved to be an aimless, unpivoted, chartless soul, drifting nowhere in particular and with no least conception of either the order or the thoroughgoing intellectual processes of life, and yet not wholly uninteresting to me. Why, I often wondered. In so far as I could see he picked only vaguely at or fumbled unintelligently with such phases and aspects of life as he encountered. He spoke persistently and yet indefinitely of the things he had seen in his travels—the mountains of the west, the plains of Texas, where he had tried to sell trees, the worth of this region in which he lived—and yet he could report only fragmentarily of anything he had ever seen. The mountains of Colorado were "purty high," the scenery "purty fine in some places." In Texas it had been hot and dry, "not so many trees in most places, but I couldn't sell any." The people he had met everywhere were little more than moving objects or figures in a dream. His mind seemed to blur almost everything he saw. If he registered any definite vital impression of any kind, in the past or the present, I could not come to know. And yet he was a suitor, as he once admitted to us via our jesting, for the hand of the much-buffeted Ida; and, as I learned later in the same year, he did finally succeed in marrying her, thus worsting the aged and no doubt much more skillful Wilkens.

Still later in the same year, it was reported to me that they were building a small house or shack on Ida's acres, and with her money, and would be in it before spring. They were working together, so the letter ran, with the carpenters, Widdle hauling lumber and sand and brick and Ida working with hammer and nails. Still later I learned that they were comfortably housed, had a cow, some pigs and chickens, a horse and various implements, all furnished by Ida's capital, and that they were both working in the fields.

The thing that interested me was the fact that at last, after so many years, having secured a man, even of so shambling a character as Widdle, the fair Ida was prone to make a god of him. And what a god.

"Gee!" one of the sons commented to me once during my stay of a few weeks the following summer. "Widdle certainly has a cinch now. He don't need to work hard any more. Ida gets up in the morning and feeds the chickens and pigs and milks the cow and gets his breakfast while he lies in bed. He works in the field plowing sometimes, but she plows, too."

"Yeah, I've seen her pitch hay into the barn from the wagon, just as she did for her father," added the second youth.

"Ah, but the difference, the difference!" mine host, the father of these same sons, was jocosely at pains to point out. "Then it was against her will and without the enabling power of love, while now—"

"Love's not gonna make hay any lighter," sagely observed one of his sons.

"No, nor plowin' any easier. Aw, haw!" This from a farm-hand, a fixture about the place. "An' I've seen her doin' that, too."

"What treachery to romance!" I chided. And otherwise did my best to stand up for romance, come what might.

Be that as it may, Widdle was about these days in a cheerful and even facetious frame of mind. When first I knew him, as a teamster, he had seemed to wear a heavy and sad look, as though the mystery of life, or perhaps better, the struggle for existence, pressed on him as much as it does on any of us. But now that his fortune had improved, he was a trifle more spruce, not so much in clothes, which were the usual farmer wear, but in manner. On certain days, especially in the afternoon, when his home chores were not too onerous or his wife was taking care of them for him, he came visiting to my woodland table on its hill, where a great and beautiful panorama spread before us. And once he inquired, though rather nibblish in his manner, as to the matter and manner of writing. Could a man make a living at that now, say? Did you have to write much or little in order to get along? Did I write for these here now magazines?

Rather ruefully I admitted that when I could I did. The way of ye humble scribe, as I tried to make plain, was at times thorny. Still, I had no great reason to complain.

We then drifted to the business of farming, and here, I confess, I felt myself to be on much firmer ground. How was he getting along? Had he made much out of his first season's crop? How was his second progressing? Did he find fifteen acres difficult to manage? Was his wife well?

To the last question he replied that she was, doing very well indeed, but as for the second from the last: "Not so very. 'Course now," he went on musingly, "we ain't got the best implements yet, an' my wife's health ain't as good this summer as 't was last, but we're gettin' along all right. I got mebbe as much as a hundred barrels o' potatas comin' along, an' mebbe three hundred bushels o' corn. For myself, I'm more interested in this here chicken business, if I could once git it agoin' right. 'Course we ain't got all the up-to-date things we need, but I'm calc'latin' that next year, if everything goes right, I'll add a new pen an' a coupla runways to the coop I got up there, an' try my hand at more chickens."

Never his wife's, I noticed, when it came to this end of the farming institution. And as an aside I could not help thinking of those breakfasts in bed and of his wife pitching hay and plowing as well as milking the cow and feeding the chickens while he slept.

The lorn Ida and her great love!

And then one day, expressing curiosity as to this

ménage, I was taken there to visit. The place looked comfortable enough—a small, unpainted, two-room affair, with a lean-to at the back for a kitchen, a porch added only the preceding spring, so that milord might have a view of the thymy valley below, with its green fields and distant hills, while he smoked and meditated. It was very clean, as I noticed even from a distance, the doorway and the paths and all. And all about it, at points equidistant from the kitchen, were built a barn, a corn-crib, a smoke-house, and a chicken coop, to say nothing of a new well-top, all unpainted as yet but all framed by the delicious green of the lawn. And Widdle, once he came forward, commented rather shyly on his treasures, walking about with me the while and pointing them out.

"What with all the other things I gotta do, I ain't got 'round to paintin' yet; but I 'low as how this comin' fall or spring mebbe I'll be able to do sumpin' on it, if my wife's health keeps up. These chickens are a sight o' bother at times, an' we're takin' on another cow next week an' some pigs."

I thought of those glum days when he was still hauling sand and stone in his squeaky wagon.

And then came Ida, big, bony, silent, diffident, red-tanned by sun and weather, to whom this narrow fifteen-acre world was no doubt a paradise. Love had at last come to her. Widdle, le grand, was its embodiment. I could not help gazing at him and then at her, for after a still, bovine fashion she seemed fond, and not only that, but respectful of him. He talked and talked, while she only spoke when addressed—never first or spontaneously. Her father's training, I thought.

It being a Sunday afternoon, the only appropriate time to make a call in the farming world, when presumably the chores of the week were out of the way, and Widdle having resumed his seat on his front porch, still she was astir among her pots and pans, though eventually she came forward and made us welcome in her shy way. Wouldn't we sit down? Wouldn't we have a glass of milk? The worthy Widdle, scarcely cognizant of her presence as it seemed to me, went on smoking and dreaming and surveying his possessions. If ever a man looked at ease, he did, and his wife seemed to take great satisfaction in his comfort. She smiled as we talked to him or answered in monosyllables when we addressed her, having been so long repressed by her father, as I assumed, that she could not talk.

But my relative had called my attention to one thing which I was to note, and that was that despite the fact that she was within three months of an accouchement, I would find her working as usual, which was true. She was obviously as near her day as that, and yet during our visit she went to look after the pigs and chickens, the while milord smoked on and talked. His one theme was the farm, his proposed addition to his chicken coop, a proposed enlargement of his pig pen, the fact that his farm would be better if he could afford to take over some five acres to the east, which were to be had, and so on. Several times he referred to his tour of the west and the fact that he had "served his time on the Denver & Rio Grande."

After that I could not help thinking of him from time to time, for he illustrated to me so clearly the casual and accidental character of so many things in nature—the fact that fortune, strength, ease, beauty, fame, any power of mind or body, come in the main to the individual as gifts and are so often not even added to or developed by any effort of his. For here was this vague, casual weakling drawn back to this region by a kind of sixth sense which regulated his well-being, mayhap, and that after he had failed in all other things, only to find this repressed and yet now free victim, his wife, seeking, by the aid of her small means, some satisfaction in the world of love through him. But did he really care for her? I sometimes asked myself that question. Could he? Had he the capacity, the power of appreciation and understanding which any worthwhile love requires? I wondered.

. . . o o . . .

The events of the following September seemed to answer the question in a rather definite way, and yet I am not so sure that they did, either. Life is so casual; love, or the matter of affinity, such an indefinite thing with so many! I was sleeping in a large room which faced the front of the house—a room which commanded the slope of a hill and a distant and splendid valley beyond. Outside were evergreens and horse-chestnuts that rustled and whispered in the slightest breeze. At two or three of the clock of one of those fine moonlit nights I heard a knocking below and a voice calling: "Oh, Mis' K——! Oh, Mis' K——!"

Fearing that my hostess might not hear, I went to one of the open windows, but as I did so the door below opened and I heard her voice and then Widdle's, though I could not make him out in the pale light. He seemed, for once, somewhat concerned, and asked if she would not come over and see his wife.

"She's been taken powerful bad all of a sudden, Mis' K——," I heard him say. "She ain't been feelin' well for the last few days; been complainin' sorta, an' she's very bad now, an' I don't know what to do. It'd be a big favor if you'd come, Mis' K——. Mis' Agnew phoned fer a doctor fer me, but she don't seem to be able to get none yet."

So Ida's time had now come! Another child—and of such parents—was about to enter the world—to be what? Do what? I wondered how the spinster-ish Ida would make out. She was rather old now for motherhood, and so large and ungainly. How would she fare? How serve a nursing child? Not many min-utes after I heard Mrs. K——, accompanied by one of her sons, leaving in the motor car, the humani-tarian and social aspects of the situation seeming to arouse in her the greatest solicitude. Then I heard nothing more until the following noon, when she returned. By that time Mrs. Widdle was very ill indeed. She had worked in the fields up to three days before, as it now appeared, and only the day before her illness had attempted to do a week's washing. No help of any kind had ever been called in, no doctor consulted. Widdle, conscious of himself only, as it appeared to me, had gone on dreaming, possibly doing his share of the work but no more, and no doubt accepting cheerfully the sacrifices and ministrations of his wife until this latest hour.

It was also evident to all that conditions underlying possible motherhood for Mrs. Widdle were most unsatisfactory. During all the nine months of gestation she had given herself no least attention. A doctor called in at this late hour by my relative wagged his head most dolefully. Perhaps she would come through all right, but there was undue pressure on the kidneys. He suggested a nurse, but this Mrs. Widdle, ill as she was, would not hear of. It would cost so much. The end came swiftly on the following night, and with great agony. She was in nowise fitted to endure the strain, and an attempt to remove the child, accompanied by uric poisoning, did for her completely. Ether was given, and she remained unconscious until she died. And the child with her.

· · · · · · ·

I saw her once, and once only, afterward, when I joined the family of my host and hostess in "viewing the body." Widdle, as I had long since learned, was in no great standing with either his relatives or his neighbors, being of that poor, drifting, dreaming caliber which offers no least foundation for a friendship, let alone a community of interest with either. Usually he was silent or slow of speech, with but a few ideas and those mostly relative to his present state upon which to meditate or speak. Consequently, few neighbors and no relatives, barring Ida's two brothers, were interested to call, and the latter in only the most perfunctory way. Such as did come or had offered assistance had arranged that the parlor, a most sacred place, should be devoted to the last ceremonies and the reception of visitors; and here the body, in a coffin, the like of which for color and decoration I had never seen before, lay in state. It was of lavender plush on the outside and lined with pink silk within, and to be carried, as one was forced to note, by six expensive handles of gilt. More, this parlor was obviously an æsthetic realm as these two had seen it, and hence arresting to any one's attention. For it was furnished with a gaudy yellow oak center table, now pushed to one side, some stiff and homely chairs with red plush seats, and a parlor wood-stove decorated with nickel and with red isinglass windows in front. On the walls, which were papered a bright pink, were two yarn mottoes handsomely framed in walnut, a picture of Widdle and his wife boxed in walnut and glass and surrounded by a wax wreath, and, for sharp contrast, a brightly colored calendar exhibiting a blonde movie queen rampant. Gracing the center table was a Bible and a yellow plush album, in which was not a single picture, for I looked. It must have been the yellow plush that had fascinated them, that ancient and honorable symbol of luxury.

But that coffin! I have no desire to intrude levity in connection with death, and, anyhow, it is said to presage misfortune. Also, I recognize too well the formless and untutored impulses toward beauty which struggles all too feebly in the most of us, animals and men. Out of such undoubtedly have risen Karnak and the Acropolis and the "Ode on a Grecian Urn." But at that time, and for all I know, the custom may endure to this hour, there was being introduced, to the poorest sections of our American big cities, and from this experience I judged to the backwoods also, this concluding gayety in the matter of coffins calculated to engage the attention of any lover of color—in short, astonishing confections in yellow, blue, green, silver, and lavender plush, usually lined with contrasting shades of silk and equipped with handles of equally arresting hues—silver, gilt, black, or gray. Trust our American profiteer Barnums of the undertaking world to prepare something that would interest the afflicted simple, if not the dead, in their hour of bereavement. Beauty, as each interprets it for himself, must certainly be the anodyne that resolves all our pains. At any rate, this coffin, as described, was piled high with garden flowers. And as I learned afterwards an attempt at

mortuary verse by Widdle, concerning which more
anon, was placed in one of his dead wife's hands.
But considering the general solidity and angularity
of the frame it held, it could not but seem incon-
gruous. Astonishing, in fact. Yet the coffin obviously
selected for its beauty and as a special comfort to the
bereaved living, the Honorable Henry Widdle. Indeed, unless I am greatly mistaken, Widdle was for
the first time in his life indulging in a long repressed
impulse toward luxury, which in its turn was disguis-
ing itself to him as deep grief.

But that figure in the coffin, the lorn Ida, no less, only
now embedded in such voluptuous materiality and at
so late a date,—she who had followed the plow and
pitched hay, and then, as a reward, had enjoyed one
toiling, closing year of love or peace, or what you will!
That hair so thick and coarse, but now smoothly plaited
and laid—red hair. The large, bony head, with wide
mouth and small nose, looking so tired. But none the
less one strong arm snugly holding the minute infant
that had never known life, close to her breast and her
big, yearning face, the other, the hand of the same—
Widdle's poem.

I turned away, arrested, humiliated, even terrified by
this fresh evidence of the blank and humorless clanking
of the cosmic urge that had brought about not only this,
but so much that is inane or miserable or horrify-
ing on this planet. For Ida's face showed lines which
stilled all humor. They were not comic and not

even sad, just fatefully mechanistic and so unbelievably grim. Sleep, I thought, sleep! It is best.

But the little house she had left, that little shell in which she had thought to intrench herself against misery and loneliness. Not a corner or a window or a shelf or a pan but had been scrubbed and shined and dusted repeatedly. The kitchen revealed a collection of utensils almost irritatingly clean; the dining-living room the same. And outside were all the things as she had left them, all in clean and orderly array. And on the front porch, viewing the scenery and greeting the few straggling visitors, Widdle himself in almost smiling serenity. For was he not now master of all he surveyed, the fifteen acres, house, barn, sheds, cattle —a man of affairs no less? And now for this great occasion in his best clothes, and looking for all the world as though he were holding a reception or conducting a function of some kind, the importance of which had been solemnly impressed upon his mind.

What interested me most, though, after seeing this other, was his attitude, the way in which he now faced death and this material as well as spiritual loss, also his attitude toward the future, now that this brief solution of most of his material difficulties had been removed. Any one who postulates the mechanical or chemical origin of life, and behaviorism as the path of its development, would have been interested in this case. As I viewed Widdle then, he was really nothing more than a weak reflection of all the

I thought not, and said so. More, that I would see what a lawyer friend of mine would have to say since he appeared much perturbed. Indeed he seemed slightly strained when he first spoke but now became more calm. Then he led me to the chicken coop and the milk house. We stood at a fence and looked over that five-acre field adjoining which some day he hoped to own. After a few more comments as to the merits of the departed, I left, and saw him but once after, some two weeks later, when, the funeral being over and the first fresh misery of his grief having passed, he came up to my table on the hilltop one sunny afternoon to spend a social moment or two, as I thought, but really to discuss the latter phases of his position as master and widower.

. . . .

The afternoon was so fine. A sea of crystal light bathed the hills and valleys, and where I worked the ground was mottled with light sifting through leaves. Birds sang, and two woodchucks, bitten by curiosity, reconnoitered my realm. Then the brush crackled, and forward came Widdle out of nowhere and sidling slightly as he came.

"Nice view you have up here."

"Yes, I enjoy it very much. Have that stump over there. How've you been?"

"Oh, pretty fair, thank you. I was thinkin' you might like to look over them papers I spoke about. I have 'em here now." And he fished in his coat pocket.

I turned over the one paper he extracted, which was a memorandum to the effect that Ida Widdle, née Hauchawout, sole owner of such-and-such property, desired and hereby agreed that in the event of her death and the absence of any children, her husband, Henry Widdle, was to succeed her as sole owner and administrator. And this was witnessed by Notary Driggs of Shrivertown.

"There's no question in my mind as to the validity of that," I solemnly assured him. "It seems to me that a lawyer could make it very difficult for any one to disturb you in your place. I can make a copy of it and find out. But why not see a lawyer? Or ask Justice Driggs?"

"Well," he said, turning his head slowly and as slowly taking the paper. "I don't like to go to any lawyer around here unless I have to nor no judge, either. They charge a lot. Besides, I'm afraid of 'em. They could make a lot o' trouble for a feller like me, not knowin' anything about these here things. But I don't calc'late to do nothin' about this unless I have to, not stir anything up, that is, but I thought you might know."

I stopped my work and meditated on his fate and how well chance had dealt with him in one way and another. Also his native shrewdness in regard to how he was to do. Lawyers, as he plainly saw, were dangerous. Judges and relatives also. After a time, during which it seemed to me that he might be thinking

I look around now and seek you in vain;
My tears they fall like rain.

The house is silent without your dear tread,
Everywhere that you were you are now missed
   instead.
I am lonely now, but our Father above
Now has you in His care and love.

If gone from me you are happy there at rest,
And death that tortures me for you is best.
Dear husband, weep not for your departed wife,
For from heaven, looking down, I see you as in
   Life.

I see your woe and grief and misery,
And would be there with you if I could in glee,
So kind you were, dear husband, and so good,
The Father of All above knows what you've
   withstood;
He knows how hard you've tried, what efforts
   you have made,
To help and serve in love. Don't be afraid.

Face the world with courage, husband dear,
And never have any fear.
For if in life you may now be misunderstood,
Our Father who is in heaven knows that you
   were kind and good.

Your efforts were very many, your rewards were
    few.
The world should know how kind you were
    and true.
The tongues of men may slander, husband dear.
But do not let that trouble your ear.
I, your wife in heaven, know how we
While we were together on earth did love and
    agree,
And in heaven too, when it pleases God to call us,
We will love and be happy together as we did on
    earth always."

He paused and looked up, and I confess that by now
my mouth had opened a little. The simplicity! The
naïve unconsciousness of possible ridicule, of anach-
ronism, of false interpretation on the part of those
who could not know! Could a mind be so obtuse as
to believe that this was not ridiculous? I stared while
he gazed, waiting for some favorable comment.

"Tell me," I managed at last, "did you write all of
that yourself?"

"Well, you know how 'tis," he proceeded to explain. "The papers round here publish these here
things right along, every week, that is. I see 'em in
The Banner, an' I just took some of the lines from
them, but a good many of 'em—most really—is my
own."

"Very good," I said encouragingly. "Excellent. But
you know you have quite a few lines there. At ten

cents a line you are going to have a big bill to pay."

"That's so," he agreed, dubiously and ruefully, at the same time scratching his head. "I hadn't thought o' that. Let's see," and he began to count. "Three dollars and forty cents," he finally announced and then fell silent.

Aha, I thought, the frailty of these earthly affections! For, looking at him as he counted up the cost of his poetic flight and thinking of his wife,—the dreary round of her days, the heavy labor up to the very hour of her death, that carefully enacted agreement as to the ultimate disposition of her property in case of her death, I could not help thinking of the pathos and futility of her as well as his life—of so much that we call life and effort, the absolute nonsense that living becomes in so many instances. Above me as I speculated was that great blazing ball we call the sun, spinning about in space and with its attendant planets. And upon the surface of this thing, "the earth," we, with our millions of little things we call "homes" and "possessions." And about and above and beneath us, immensities as well as mysteries, mysteries, mysteries. And nowhere on all the earth, not even so much as a sane guess as to what we are or what the sun is or the "reason" for our being here. And yet, passion and lust and beauty and greed and yearning, this endless pother and bitterness and delight in order to retain this elusive and inexplicable something, "life," "us," "ours," in space. Birds a-wing, trees blowing and whispering, fields teeming with mysterious and yet needed things, and then, on every hand this wealth of tragedy. Life living on life, men and animals plotting and scheming as though there were only so much to be had and all of that in the possession of others.

And yet, despite the mystery and the suffering and the bitterness, here was this golden day, an enormous treasure in itself, and these lovely trees, these mountains blue, this wondrous, soothing panorama. Beauty, beauty, beauty, appealing and consoling to the heart—life's anodyne. And here, in the very heart of it, Ida Hauchawout, and her father, with his "no enimel gets fet py me," and his son who threw a pitch-fork at him, and this poor clown before me with his death-rhymes now apparently too expensive and his fear of losing the little that had been left to him. *His* love. *His* loss. *His* gain. *His* desire to place *him*self right before the "world." Ha, ha! Ho, ho! This was what he was rhyming about. This was what he was worrying about.

But was he guilty of any wrong before the world? Not a bit that I could see. Was he entitled to what he had come by? As much as any of us are entitled to anything. Yet here he was, worrying, worrying, worrying, and trying to decide in the face of his loss or gain whether his verse, this tribute or self-justification, was worth three dollars and forty cents to him as a display in a miserable, meagerly circulated and quickly forgotten country newspaper.

Mesdames and Messieurs, are we all mad? Or am I?

Or is *Life?* Is the whole thing what it appears to be to so many—aimless, insane, accidental jumble and gibberish? We articulate or put together out of old mysteries new mysteries, machines, methods, theories. But to what end? What about all the Hauchawouts and Widdles, past, present, and to come, their sons, daughters, and relatives, and all the fighting and the cruelty and the parading and the nonsense?

The crude and defeated Ida. And this fumbling, seeking, and rather to be pitied dub with his rhymes. Myself, writing and wondering about it all.

. . . .

A letter written several years later by my relative's wife added this for my enlightenment:

"I think you ought to know that Widdle has been taken with religon and now interprets the Bible in his own fumbling way, coming to me occasionally for help. He plows his fields and meditates, expecting God any minute to come in the form of a dragon or giant and finish him and all men. He has figured out that the world will come to an end in this wise: God will appear as a dragon or a gigantic man, and wherever he places his foot, there life will cease to exist. That will be the end of the world. Yet he has no notion that the world is any larger than the United States at most. I said to him once: 'But Widdle, it would take Him a long time to step over all the world and crush out all life, wouldn't it?' 'Yes, that's so,' he replied, 'but I guess His feet are bigger than ours—

maybe as big as a barn, an' mebbe He can walk faster than we can.' He has lost himself completely in the Bible now and reads and meditates all the time, applying everything he reads to his own few acres. He still lives alone and does his own cooking, fearing, I think, a second wife who might take his possessions from him. But no legal trouble has ever been made him. People are a little sorry for him, I think. His chief dish is cornmeal mush, which he boils and pours into saucers or flat plates to the thickness he wants, because he doesn't know how to pour it into a deep dish and slice it."

EMANUELA

Emanuela

A TEMPERAMENT and a life that cannot be driven from one's mind provokes thought. Hence this.

In my early semi-bohemian but more strictly working days in New York there breasted that trying literary sea a certain group of young aspirants which often referred to her as "Our Lady of the Snows," "The Iceland Venus," "Madonna della Kamchatka" and similar semi-critical, semi-laudatory characterizations. And my word for it, in a cold, virginal, intellectual way she was beautiful as Minerva must have been beautiful. Young, too—not more than twenty. Nevertheless, despite those still, intellectual and examining if not exactly icy blue eyes and the gold-brown hair that like a lovely silken wreath encircled her forehead, I was critical. How could anyone so beautiful, so voluptuously formed, be so indifferent to every eligible and likable youth within her ken? No visible emotional interest in any one! Only thoughts, lofty thoughts, and always, in so far as she was concerned, refined and yet forceful argument. She was so interested in making the world a better place. And yet, the smoothness and soft provoking roundness of her cheeks and neck and arms and body; the moving and yet so elusive lift of the eyebrows above the high, waxy forehead. Verily, a

Greek girl, I thought, come to New York in this year of our Lord out of the depths of one of the most comfortable if not exactly fastidious homes of northern conservative Illinois—Wheaton, to be exact—and destined, possibly, by her brains and beauty to make a stir.

Her desire and intention, as I gathered at the time, was to write—first, short stories and later novels and plays. Her presence in the limited and at that time wholly undistinguished group of egotists struggling for existence in the region of Washington Square was due to the belief that in part and along with other phases of the great city we constituted "local color" of an artistic and literary flavor, from which, as she herself once told me, one gathered, or might, criticism, verification, and so enthusiasm and strength for one's own ideas. Have I not said that she was highly intellectual?

At the same time there was slumbering in her somewhere, (in her "subconscious," as Freud would have said, I am sure!), a suspicion or conviction that although life was to be learned from life, and that in order to create art one must interpret the actual in some form which would awaken a response in those who had been or were in contact with the actual, still, studying life at first hand and knowing it as a writer, did not necessarily mean knowing all of it. There were, as she once explained, (not to me but to a fellow-aspirant with whom she chanced to enter into an argument in my presence), depths or phases of life and thought to which an aspiring writer, of however

great talent or genius, need not and therefore should
not descend. (I was sure at the time that one arrow of
her quiver was meant for me.) Also that facts and
phases there were which were decidedly beyond the
provinces of art or mental illumination in any direction.
But to all of this the writer with whom she was
arguing—and who has since become famous—replied
that she was wrong, that she would better read some
of the writings and experiences of the really great
writers and poets and painters. Whereupon more argument as to who were the really great writers—Scott
and Dickens and Thackeray and George Eliot and
Hugo (as represented by "Les Misérables") or Tolstoi,
Turgenev, Flaubert, de Maupassant, Balzac, Zola,
Fielding, D'Annunzio (already in translation with
"The Triumph of Death"). Naturally, the arguers split
on the question of material and an author's "right" to
his material. As Emanuela—the heroine of this story—
saw it, neither Sophocles (in "Œdipus Rex") nor Fielding (in "Tom Jones") nor D'Annunzio (in "The
Triumph of Death") nor Balzac (in "Cousin Betty")
nor de Maupassant had any right to take for analysis,
let alone dwell upon the same at novel or play length,
the grosser and hence baser passions of mankind. Not
that such things might not be understood (at a distance) or touched upon even by way of illustrating
right from wrong and illuminating the paths of evil
and failure, but to dwell upon them, as in the case of
Zola . . . faugh! Or to fall from grace in even one

work, as in the case of Tolstoi ("The Kreutzer Sonata"), of Flaubert ("Madame Bovary"), when the same writers could and did write such great books as "War and Peace" or "Salammbô" . . . Ah, what an error lay in that!

Positively, as she uttered these conservative *obiter dicta* the while I sat to one side and contemplated her physical pulchritude, I was astonished. To think, as I there and then said to myself, that any one so shrewd and observant as well as attractive as this charming Emanuela should fail to grasp the central significance of sex in life, its enormous and so often deranging force. Had she really within herself no indicative passions, or moods even, which might serve, however determinedly she might seek to avoid the leer of the satyr in us all, to guide her toward a clearer perception as to what it is that motivates the most of us? I could scarcely believe that she was so set in so emasculate a version of the good, the true, and the beautiful. And yet, there she was talking as she was.

Among those who observed and frequently criticized her—yet secretly admired her, I am sure—was one Ernest Scheib, we will call him, a young writer fresh from Dakota, with talent aplenty and dreaming of literary fame in New York. His subsequent mental eclipse by insanity depressed me as much as any tragedy I have ever contemplated. At the time he, and occasionally Emanuela, was part of a group that rotated about a painter, Munchhof by name, then living and working in Washington Square, a dynamic and vivid Westerner who drew to himself all types—illustrators, playwrights, architects, editors, poets, frequently more potential than placed.

Now the thing about Scheib that interested me was that he was poetic as well as realistic—one of those rare colorful temperaments out of our soil and light that occasionally belies the darkling, material American scene. He was so young, so tentative in so many of his approaches, so attractive and romantic, at the same time that he was solidly, after the fashion of Balzac or de Maupassant, enamored of reality. And yet, in the face of this girl's coldly puritanic reactions, or perhaps because of them, he was drawn to her, though (because of her own attitude toward him, probably) bitterly critical at times.

"She a writer!" he once said to me sourly as he passed out after one of our meetings, and possibly because she had repulsed his advances. "What does she think she is going to write about? People who live as she thinks they do? And have real people praise her? Toodle-waddle!" Innocent that he was, Scheib was firmly convinced that some day, and soon, the current and all-enveloping romanticism must give way to a sound and sincere picturing of life.

But in spite of his criticism of her, Emanuela prospered, whereas he, and myself, did not. For in addition to her beauty she was possessed of a practical insight which enabled her to construct various informative as well as instructive articles tending to demonstrate the onward-and-upwardness of the world in many ways. And how the current magazines of that day devoured such things. Also a suave type of puritan romance which she considered realism and which presented some dear old father, or mother, or sister, or brother, or what have you, doing the right thing at the right moment to save somebody in some dramatic and, from a moral point of view, most satisfactory way. Once in Munchhof's studio in Washington Square, on a pleasant sunny afternoon, Scheib, sitting at one of the front windows overlooking the Square and reading the then all-too-widely distributed *Saturday Evening Post,* suddenly burst forth with "Hell" at the same time casting said widely circulated medium to the floor.

"And who has disagreed with us now?" observed Munchhof calmly the while he stepped back to eye the painting he was absorbedly retouching.

"What a damn fool that girl is!" went on Scheib, without indicating whom—though by this time we knew he referred to Emanuela and one of her stories. "Such rot! An honorable family friend saves a wayward girl from herself—by a few kind words!" He kicked the paper still further away.

"Evidently you don't believe in the good intentions of kind friends where wayward girls are concerned," observed Simondson, a young editor. Scheib made no reply.

"The trouble with Ernest is," went on Munchhof,

"he's jealous of Emanuela. She gets in the *Post* and he doesn't." He cackled irritatingly.

"Oh, you guys give me a pain!" replied Ernest, sourly. (He was referring to the editorial tribe.) "It's the whole damned magazine game that's no good. You're all trying to find some silly, conventional stuff that your readers will like, and any fool that will come along and write it for you gets in." At this Simondson rose and bowed for his profession. "And that's what makes her so cocky about her notions of how things are. She gets 'em published." His lips curled scornfully.

"One word, Scheib," pleaded Munchhof artfully, for it looked as though Scheib were leaving then and there. "Pardon me. If she were nice to you, what about her then?"

"Oh, hell!" retorted Scheib, and went out.

"I'm sure he's struck on her at that," insisted Munchhof, who was a fair judge of Homo Sapiens. "He takes too much interest in her."

And believe it or not, this wounded me painfully, for whether she was interested in Scheib or not, I was interested in her and was dreaming wild dreams of what seemed at the time an impossible friendship with her.

"She is attractive, and that probably helps her get a hearing," went on Simondson, who now had no Scheib to hear him. "But if her stuff weren't valuable, she couldn't get it published."

"Valuable to one of your popular magazines," sneered some one else—possibly myself.

"I can always scratch Scheib," went on Munchhof, "by insisting that he can't write as well as she can. But anyhow, we won't see much of her around here any more. I hear she's joined the A. Club and the National Arts. That means she won't spend much time here."

At that I noticed Scheib, who had suddenly returned for something, pause and look at Munchhof, although his only comment was: "Is that so?" But I had the feeling that there was much more than light indifference behind his look. And let me confess it here. This look of Scheib's did not cheer me. He was younger, better-looking, and there were not a few girls who found him attractive. Might not Emanuela eventually turn to him? And then what? She would be gone from me forever. She could marry Scheib easily enough. And although I did not care for her dogmatic moralizing, I was not so sure but that I, (I bow), if she would only be so kind as to take an interest in me, might not be able to change her, make her see life in a different and more liberal way. (The vanity of me!) For beautiful she was. Often I sat and looked at her milk and rose complexion, her soft hair and gray-blue eyes, and marveled that any one so physically perfect could hold such perverse views. And occasionally she and I argued, but never in the blatant way of Scheib and some of the others, since for once in my life, and because I had an object in view, I tried

not to affront her imaginings concerning life. Rather
I even faintly praised her stories, or if not that, said
things which were calculated to make her feel that
they were not as conventional, and so worthless, as I
felt them to be.

And then a lapse of time. And in spite of my interest
I did not see her as often as I desired. She was here,
she was there. With the money she was making from
stories and articles, as well as—or so I understood—an
income derived from her parents, she could travel to
places to which neither Scheib nor I nor any of this
group could go at this time—Europe, New England,
the south in winter. More, she appeared to be part and
parcel of one of those smart and editorially successful,
self-impressed and self-assertive groups of intellectuals
who from time to time, as is the case in every capital,
achieve the spotlight and beat the drum.

But after a year or so—myself having achieved an
editorship of sorts by then, who should arrive on the
scene but Emanuela and, looking me, or rather my
magazine, up as a market. And—the magazine being
what it was—popular—I finding some of her stuff
available . . . Result, we were soon, and for the first
time, on easy and even genial terms. More, there were,
of course, various literary and art functions about town
at which I now found myself meeting her. And still
more, as I hereby confess, to some of these I most definitely went in the hope of encountering and contact-
ing her more intimately. Her beauty, in spite of all this

time, still captivated me. Unfortunately, as I hereby report, I still found her too respectable and prosperous, too much fortified by the world from which she derived, to pay any particular attention to me. At the same time, there was there a refinement and interest in things beautiful and intelligent which, coupled with her charm, made me persist in my attempt to fascinate her. But also, and always in connection with me, there was an elusiveness, sometimes, as it seemed to me, a critical, and so defiant, or emotionally recessive and even fearful attitude, which troubled and even angered me. For occasionally, when we met or were dancing or talking, there was warmth as well as a sudden and seemingly illuminating *nearness* in her eyes which caused me to think "She likes me" or "she might." Sometimes, as I thought, it appeared to be even more than that, as though and at last she was about to admit to a real emotion. At such moments, however, I was likely to become too impetuous or too intense, and venture upon some purely emotional compliment, whereupon and instantly, she would change. That old and purely intellectual frigidity would return, the unusual warmth and color of the moment before evaporate completely. I could see it fade from her eyes, and would then experience a mental chill, which, as experience proved, was sufficient to drive me from her for weeks.

At last, in a kind of fury against these encouraging approaches and freezing recessions, I said: "Oh the devil! Why bother? I cannot make anything out of her. Either she likes me or she doesn't. But if she does, let her finally find out for herself in some way. I cannot go on like this, and I won't." And so I really did my best to withdraw. And she, no doubt sensing something of my mood and feelings—some criticism of herself therein—would let me go for months at a time—in several instances for as many as six—when some chance encounter, bringing us together again, we would go through the same thing and of course separate as before. Yet as I also noticed and for all her beauty she did not marry. Rather, many who knew and admired her not only for her beauty but her mind, spoke of her as too cold. Once Munchof, who kept more or less in touch with her and myself, said to me: "There's something wrong with Emanuela. She's either undersexed or too purely mental, or something. You can't tell me that a girl as beautiful as she is wouldn't have married or had an affair with some one by now. It isn't natural. I always thought she should have been drawn to Scheib, really."

A sharp pang in me at this. Scheib! My old and yet younger rival! And as much as I cared for him personally, how much I resented his possible interest in Emanuela or hers in him! But of course all that was dead now, for him and for me.

And yet, just about this time—not more than three or four months later—a most interesting thing in connection with him and Emanuela and myself. I should

say here, in connection with Scheib, that like
Emanuela, and throughout all this time, he had really
been one of the sharp, almost poignant interests in my
life, for I admired him so, perhaps even loved him.
That glassy, water-clear mind of his; its glacial and
yet so colorful and truthful reflections of life (art,
letters, men, events). Commercially or materially or
practically, as you will, he was seemingly making no
progress, selling almost nothing. And in consequence
not eating as regularly as he might, or dressing as
warmly as he needed to. And yet the quality
of the few things he wrote! The quiet, deprived and
yet unresentful meditation on the type of thing he
should do; the slow, painstaking way in which he was
trying to formulate something—a type of short story
which should be an exquisite distillation of a vast and
moving reality.

And how often, although he was twenty-four to my
thirty-four, I went to seek him out in his bleak little
room in Sullivan Street south of Washington Square.
His attitude stoic, unabashed and unashamed, fascinated me. Ha, life! What did anything matter?
Clothes, food, entertainment?— Everything was entertaining and important. Love? It was a singular
thing, it had not affected him much as yet, he was
glad to report. In case it did he would be interested to
study its effects. True, he was moved by beauty in
many ways—a dancing child, a girl's hair blowing
about her eyes. But man's true distinction was in the

realm of intensive thought. His glory was to explore this mystery about him. All else was folly—shoddy—muddy degradation. He would none of it. And so enamored of him was I in those thin, new, exploring days that I used to wish that I might take his spare, tempestuous, ironic body and soul in my arms and mother it. And there were others who felt as I did and who, through me, saw to it that he did not want. There were ways past all his suspicions of reaching him with what he needed until he could make his way for himself.

But then, and to the horror and misery of all of us, a great calamity. *The* great calamity for him. Insanity. For it now appeared that he was part of a family with a psychiatric history. His father mad, had died by his own hand. An aunt, a great-grandfather, insane. And now Scheib! Genius, and insanity! That fair Hamlet-like mind. It began, as I was told, with delusions of danger. One of us who loved him most was seeking his life. A little later on, it was another who wished to circumvent his literary career. Also he now had a philosophy—the key to all thought. Eureka, it explained everything! But into whose hands might he trust it? And then, and at the same time almost, delusions of grandeur. He was rich. He was famous and powerful. He could order things and his commands would be obeyed. I cannot go into the long, depressing story. It took time and loving care to place him where he would not be ill-used.

But now as for Emanuela and himself—her part in this amazing development. One day in the second or grand stage of his state, he appeared at Emanuela's door—and when he had never so much as once been there before. (Or so she said.) At that time she did not know that he had lost his mind. Nor did I. But from somewhere—possibly a magazine—he had secured her address, and now, gloriously enough, he was the daring adventurer, the captain and master of his life and the lives of others. And for the first time—openly, that is—it appeared that Emanuela was the all-desired. His intention, as he explained to her on her opening the door, was to take her to St. Kitts in the Barbados and marry her. He had a yacht. They were to possess a plantation. And whatever her mood, there was to be no escape on her part. Look, he was armed! And he produced a knife. She must come quietly, no sign to anybody. There was a taxi downstairs, he had brought it.

Terrified and flattered, as she explained to me afterwards, she went with him. He was so wild and yet in his madness attractive. There was about him that that evoked respect as well as sympathy. Besides now he declared a great love for her. He had always loved her, he said. She had scorned him, but never mind now. Come, he was master! She would do as he said, as his love ordered. And in a confusion of terror and wonder, with no help immediately at hand, she did accompany him, she walking before, he behind. But

bethinking herself at each step how to do, what to
say. If only some man would come up the stairs or
an officer be standing in the street!

And then, as she said, an inspiration! What about
clothes? Money? Most poorly dressed he was, always.
And so, once seated in the taxi, she decided on her
course. Would he not permit her, since she had nothing to wear, first to stop at a bank and cash a check?
Afterwards he might come with her to a store and
help her select a few things. He could not expect her
to go this way, surely. After studying her with suspicious eyes, as she related, he at last said yes, he would.
But let her remember that he was at hand! One word,
one gesture—he showed the knife he had brought.
Hence more thought, and a cold terror on her part
as they rode. Then at the bank in Fifth Avenue, he
getting out first and elaborately conducting her to the
door. And once inside following her to a counter
where under his eyes she wrote a check. But now
what? Fortunately for her, there was a woman's booth
or anteroom into which she had to go to cash her
check, but not without imploring him to understand
that it must be so. Would he not wait at the door?
And then he standing at the door, she before the teller's window, murmured, she said: "Please, please make
no sign. That man at the door is mad. Do something!
He may kill me!" And at once, while the teller appeared to be studying the check, the guard signal and
two guards coming up behind Scheib and seizing him.

But with Scheib looking over his shoulder and calling to Emanuela: "You did this. But you'll come with me yet. I will be back." Yet never coming back after that, to her or to any one.

But the import of all this to me at that time! For despite Munchhof's reiterated jibe that Scheib really cared for Emanuela, I never really believed, or perhaps better, wished not to believe it. But now here was the proof—this visit of his to her when there were so many others he had met. Then we had been indulging in an identical passion. Or was it that? For despite her resistance, if not complete indifference, I had been living well enough. There were others who were not so cold. But Scheib! That austere soul. So lonely and perhaps thinking of her more passionately than ever I could. And now he was mad, safely incarcerated in an asylum where he could never trouble her or me any more, whereas I, unless there were others preceding me in her interest . . .?

The months passed—a year—two years. During this interval Emanuela went abroad and apart from an occasional letter or card I did not hear of her. But such letters! Always brief and about some intellectual adventure somewhere. A certain Gordon Craig had established an experimental theater somewhere in Italy and she was investigating that, interested by the pure art of it. A certain Jacques Delcroze had developed Eurythmics and was teaching them to inspired disciples somewhere. She was there. There was a cele-

brated American dancer with a school in Greece or
Rome—I forget where—she was there. But never a
word about love for anybody or the possibility of marriage. Just mind, mind, mind, the advancement of art
through thought—cold, emotionless thought—or so I
insisted to myself always.

But then, after an absence of two years, her return.
She had been called back by something in connection
with her family, which much later I learned about.
A little later she resumed her characteristic relations
with those who so changefully and yet perennially
make up the active art forces of New York. And despite those who had quit or ceased to try or were dead
or married, here she was again in touch with things
as before, only now some five or six years older and
apparently as uninvolved emotionally as ever. And in
one sense that was a comfort; in another not, since it
argued some emotional defect.

But by now I was no longer an editor, having retired
to resume my literary activities. And not at all in touch
with her save by hearsay. But just the same, for some
complicated reason, partially connected with a self-
resented liking or desire for me, maybe, an invitation
from her. She was at such and such an address. And
with so much to report,—travels, experiences, etc. But
now I answered not. I could not believe it would come
to anything and I no longer desired her arms-length
friendship—or so I thought. But next, since I no longer
troubled to respond—having been free of her so long

and being weary of criticism, real or implied—a gingerly visit to my abode. She had come to see what I was doing. She had heard that I was working on another novel, and she would so like to read it and make some suggestions if I would permit. She had always thought—and she was sure she was right—that if I would only listen to certain suggestions, not necessarily from her, of course, but from some one, she did feel that I ought to talk to her or some one. Whereupon a mental row in which I all but destroyed her, as I thought. Yet with herself walking about my place with the air of one who was saying: "Now you must not think I am going to stay very long. Nor will I make myself comfortable for fear it might be misinterpreted. There is an interest here, of course, but this is purely social. . . ." This damned woman, I thought. Will she never let me be?

Yet her appearance! The clothes! The careful grooming! A smartness which, as I thought at the time, certainly did for the notion that a woman writer could not be beautiful. And an aroma of what? Could all her thought be as severely intellectual as she seemed to wish to indicate? What is there back of all this if not a basic sensual desire? Else why should she follow me up in this way? And yet now here as always boring me with comment concerning style—some school or laboratory or movement in connection with which she chanced to be interested and views concerning which she brought. Yet in this talk, as in others before and after, falling afoul of life or morality or reality, and disagreeing, of course. Yet moved by the smooth, velvety freshness of her cheeks and chin and forehead, the roundness of her neck and arms, the liquid serenity of her eyes, and myself drawing near as usual, too near as she saw it. Whereupon, sensing and recoiling from the reconnoitering acquisitiveness of me, herself congealing and preparing to leave. There was something she had to do, some one to see. Whereupon from the depths of my being, anathemas excommunicating her and all evasive or puritanic beauty everywhere forever! Damn her! Never, never again should she be admitted to my presence! Never, never again one simple interested thought on my part to be sent in her direction! Never!

And so a few months of silence, separation and seeming indifference, with occasional thoughts as indicated by cards from her straying my way. Cards from Cape Cod, Quebec, Brittany, craving my attention for the beauty of these places. Yet no word from me, although plenty of thoughts. And now and then I found myself reading an occasional story or article by her in some magazine and damning her out as usual for her truly recalcitrant and wholly unilluminating point of view.

But then fall coming on and people coming back, other things there were which tended to revive this connection. For instance, there was the A. Club party which I attended and to which she came, a seraph in white. I recall a completely enveloping seamless blue velvet cloak which she opened at the neck and let fall to the floor and out of which she stepped as out of a blue basin. The accidental contact had its usual effect, and I showed it, whereupon, evasively she receded but talked of coming to see me. (Never, I asserted to myself, and went away.)

But later a letter to inform me of a new address. She had taken, experimentally, one of the new model tenement apartments on the East Side. A wonderful atmosphere. I must come and see what was being done for the poor workingman or tenement dwellers,— she being psychically if not actually one and the same with all of them. At any rate, she was gathering "material" or local color out of which she imagined (or so I sneered) she was later going to build a great slum-dwellers' novel. I think I damned her heartily for that. The watery-veined, lily-livered this and that! Yet believe it or not, and thinking of the white dress and the flowerlike face and grace as evinced at the A. Club, I journeyed to the East Side, a second friendly letter being the cause. She had such a really quaint and delightful place, she wrote. It was so different from Washington Square. Here were the towers of Williamsburg and Manhattan Bridges in full view. And in the distance, south and north, various commercial towers as well as the lights and sights of East River. Just above her was the roof, yet no one ever venturing up there. Too

much real air and beauty and silence. And she herself would cook the dinner. And we could sit up on
the roof afterwards and look down on the sights and
sounds. She said nothing of a girl medical student
room-mate who would be back at eleven, or that the
place was furnished after the best Washington Square
fashion of the hour—paintings, loaned statuary, and
books, etc.

I journeyed and was enchanted by the crowded, hot
streets of a stifling June night. Summer seemed
fluttering by like a velvety, black-winged moth. From
the roof, as she said, could be seen the lights and the
great towers. And the stars seemed to reach down to
the lamps of the river. And Emanuela, in white organdie and an apple-green apron, hurrying here and
there and actually preparing a dinner for me while she
talked of art or took me to the roof or recounted the
wonders of reality as evinced by the poor sweat-shop
Jews who gasped for air in the smelly streets below. I
found her warm, exotic, more human and girl-like
than ever I had seen her before. She seemed mentally
close and emotionally affectionate.

Yet on the roof after dinner, what? She seemed so
near to a rapturous life mood with me that at last I
seized her, pulled her close to me, put my lips to hers.
But as usual she was struggling, pulling away, and
adding at the same time: "Don't! Stop! Oh, please! I
don't like you this way! Please, don't!" And an almost
angry bound like a fighting cat. Whereupon this time

I said things angry, half ugly. What a fool she was!
Did she really know anything that she wanted? Did
she? And anyhow all this bother just for a dinner! The
letters, the organdie dress, the gay wide green sash
that held it, the apron! Why all this nonsense for a
conservative social chat with me? Why not her room-
mate and six others as chaperons?

Just the same, and in the face of all this, she was
still stubborn and cold. If I couldn't behave, very well.
She certainly hadn't thought of what I was thinking
—this final close contact. Never! She hadn't thought of
me in that way. Couldn't. True, she liked me, but for
my mind. (Not my looks, not even my books, you see.
They were this, that, defective as art.) But if I could
not see her as a warm, helpful, mental companion, one
who would always love to talk with and be near me
and one with whom I could talk . . . I finally strode
out, saying to her as to myself that this was the last.
She was not to write me any more or bother me in any
way. And then as I went along the crowded streets,
thinking—not even a kiss. Not even a loving embrace.
And she the exquisite, blossomy thing that she is! I
frowned and shrugged my shoulders for days.

Yet, and this in spite of myself and her, I was not
through with her either. Far from it. For once the
following winter, at an A. Club dance, there she was,
in the gusty foyer, slipping out of a heavy, blood-red
velvet cloak like the blue one of the year or so before.
And for me as alluring as ever! Those serene, blue-

gray eyes. That smooth down-like complexion. And she strode as Diana might. Despite our quarrel she came up to me. How had I been? Was I in the same place? She had been here or there, was not down in the East Side any more, just now living with her mother who was visiting her here in New York. Her mother would be stopping by for her presently, around eleven-thirty. Wouldn't I like to meet her? She would like her to meet me. And meanwhile, if I would, we might dance. Yes?

Rather sourly, considering our last conversation, and yet with an irresistible glow, too, I agreed. Surely. Also I would be glad to meet her mother. And yet why, as I was asking myself, should I be pleased to meet either her or her mother? Hadn't I agreed with myself never to bother with her again? I pumped up quite a dislike, and except for another girl who was dwelling here in the club and whom I was to join later, I would have left.

Yet, later in the evening, seeing her coming toward me again, I melted. There was something about her, as cold as she was, that evoked hope. If only I could break that mood of hers—make her like me enough! If only that Minerva-esque armor of intellect, research intellect, could be pierced! Positively, there was that about her rounded arms, her neck and waist and thighs and breasts, that evoked passionate lightnings. There would be thoughts, as direct as light, as weakening as heat, that would flash past—thoughts that showed us alone and revealed the one to the other. Yet she resisting; I at last conquering. And it was as though I were victorious for the least fraction of a second; also, and on account of that, as though I could not endure the pain of so wanting and not having. And with this would come resentment, and even hate, the desire to say some rough or sneering thing and then turn and walk away. Yet even as she approached there would be this blinding wish to win her, and so I would wait. And we would dance together and look at each other. And I would think of some intimate question to ask, but because of what had been so far, refrain and then hate her, even wish to strike her.

And on this occasion, as before, I was disappointed, and yet not wholly so. Something in her manner, a certain warmth or unction which yet carried no words to match it pervaded the contact. Or perhaps I imagined so. But she did say that she had wanted to write, only she was afraid to. I was so difficult. She had so many warm impulses toward me, friendly or affectionate, yet all inhibited by my determination to read something into her that was not there. And really now, wasn't it possible for me to like some one—a girl like herself, say—without wishing or being determined to make her do what she did not wish to do? There was something about sex—she would confess it—that made her sick, deathly sick, to even think of. Did I understand that? Could I? I wondered and wondered whether she was lying—but without grasping the ob-

vious pathologic fact in her case, that she was frigid
and yet not so—fighting an almost hopeless inhibition
which I had not sense enough or courage enough to
break for her. But even so, her beauty! Could
not this strange evasion be overcome? I even speculated
as to whether it might not be possible for me, the circumstances being what they were, to indulge in a
happy camaraderie which should consist of walks
and talks and confidences, brother and sister-wise,
without wishing to carry it further than that. But no!
What nonsense! What lunacy! And I told her so. Men
were not like that. I was not. She would not like me
that way if I were. She was indulging in some unnatural, hopeless, futile dream. In God's name, what was
all her physical beauty for?

"You are so difficult," was all she said at the time.

"I am," I replied.

The reëncounter died away in, on her part, cool half-
resentment, on mine in a kind of defeated hate. Yet
just as I was leaving she was back again. Her mother
had arrived. Didn't I want to come and meet her?
Please. She had told her mother of me. I looked at her,
thinking why the devil is it that I cannot persuade this
Venus to something more than a mental camaraderie?
And so thinking, walking with her to meet her mother,
yet saying *for the last time in this world!* And then
bowing to and shaking hands with a short, stout, hard,
dull, and yet carefully and expensively dressed woman,
thin-lipped, square-browed, unimaginative and socially

correct, who looked at me as she might at some young candidate for her daughter's hand.

Now one of the thoughts that held me at the time was this—that while it was passing strange that such beauty and intelligence as Emanuela's should emanate from such a source, still perhaps this was likewise the source of her emotional chill as well as her sex inhibitions. For what could this woman give a daughter in the way of emotion or warmth? Nothing! On the other hand, it was interesting to see how humanly fond Emanuela was of this numbskull, for obviously her mother was a conventional numbskull, whereas Emanuela, as remote as she might be from a realistic concept of life, was still miles from such thoughts as her mother was entertaining. Yet along with an obvious fondness for her mother one could sense in Emanuela an intellectual tolerance which was in part amusing because of the source from which it derived. Indeed, it was interesting to see them together. I found myself assuming that the father must be better than the mother, surely, else no such daughter as this.

And then sometime later—the following spring, I think—I met her father. This was on Fifth Avenue and they were shopping. He was tall, well-built, handsome, but as I saw at once of a decidedly conservative and close-mouthed type or turn—your calculating yet conventional lawyer lured by social place as well as financial and legal success and careful of his every thought and word—so much so that I could not help feeling that I was talking to a legal as well as social automaton. His real thoughts, if any, were not for any one but himself. And exactly the husband of the mother I had seen. A safe—and so far as Chicago and Wheaton, Illinois, were concerned—politely successful lawyer. In fact, long before this I had gathered that Emanuela's home in Wheaton had been the center for much conventional as well as partially religious uplift. She had once admitted as much to me. Also that one of the deepest regrets of her father and mother as well as their friends had been that she had chosen to forsake Wheaton and marriage for New York and its pitfalls or evils, literature being one of the same.

After seeing her in the company of her father, and remembering her mother, I decided that no real personage could spring from such a union, and tried as usual to forget her. But I could not. Her mere symmetry and texture and some deep-seated and not to be surfaced desire of hers would reach me and I would think of her as not wholly glacial and so not wholly unobtainable. Surely, surely! And suppose one could reach to her? The thought of it was so inflammable at times that I would find myself in a kind of rage thinking of her and life, its persistent interpositions and evasions which left one like myself so constantly and fruitlessly hoping.

And then, her mother's health failing—or so she thought—there was a long trip somewhere, a two years' stay. And after that a meeting in New York with me for lunch and to see an exhibit somewhere, but really to restore this hopeless and, as I saw it, useless contact. For it was fully eight years now since I had first met Emanuela. And while she was still beautiful and desirable, as I saw it, she was not getting any younger. And one characteristic thing about this reunion—she was on her way, and taking me, too, to see a collection of dreamy and sensuous paintings by one Arthur B. Davies. Gracile nudes strewn or draped like flowers on a starlit summer lawn. Lily-like nudes faltering here and there in dreams or in sleep. Seeking and sensuous nudes straining upward with their bodies and arms and faces like flowers, bodies and arms that seemed to me to be seeking light and air, freedom and delight above the muddy and dank repressions of the day or the world in which they found themselves.

"But how can you like such things, Emanuela?" I commented. "You know you have no interest in the creative processes of life. Where men and women are concerned, you invariably evade or deny." (I am not pretending to the actual words but to the substance of what I said.) "You are always here and there looking at God knows what—Eurythmic dancers, paintings like these . . . But why? When it comes to reality, your personal relation to such things, you are not there. Even in your work there is nothing of anything like this. But if you're so interested, why isn't there?"

And then, as usual, she turned on me with comments about myself. I was this, that, lacking in so very many necessary inhibitions, not constructed to sense, let alone observe, the necessary refinements and nuances of organized social life. A long and severe charge. Whereupon I flared: And who was she to be talking to me? And why pursue me through the years? Had I sought her out? Either she knew what she wanted or she didn't. If she did or didn't, please stay away from me in the future. I could not endure any longer this silly palaver about social inhibitions, especially from a woman of her type. What a pity Scheib, at the time he called on her and as mad as he was, had not been able to force her to a contact with reality! And then I strode out, never, as I hoped, to be bothered by her again.

Yet still I was not done with her, or she with me. For the following year, having taken a studio in a summer art colony near New York—in New Jersey then— she was back with an invitation. It was a most inviting spot—Doornvelt in Rockland County. A most amusing art group lived and worked there. Her particular studio was placed two miles to the east, so one might truly argue that it was or was not a part of that cottage world, but on the Edgecomb or western slope, which was the great attraction for her, and overlooking the Edgecomb River. A pretty brook ran directly beneath her southern window. And she and a certain Rosalie Somebody had taken it for the summer, only recently Rosalie had been compelled to go somewhere else for a few weeks and except for a servant and occasional guests she was alone. And now wouldn't I like to come out for a few days? It was true that we had quarreled, but never mind that. It was a place that would delight my soul, whether I liked her or not. But surely I could forgive and forget that last quarrel. She was sorry, as she always was. Besides, there were some attractive girls here—more attractive than she was—and I should be introduced or not, as I chose.

But the great thing was the beauty of the place and the chance to rest. A great bare, bowldered slope above the cabin climbed to a height of six hundred feet. And below the cabin and the green field which surrounded it the river, sparkling these August nights in the moon. Didn't I want to come, for a week or for as long as I chose, really? There was plenty of room in this place. Besides, if I desired I could have a tent all to myself down by the river, in a clump of silver birches—a nice, warm, dry tent, where I could write or rest or play. And Sigrid, her Swedish servant, would cook for me, bring my breakfast, or she herself would prepare and serve it and eat it with me. And she would promise not to intrude in any way, nor should we quarrel. She would not let me quarrel, or rather would not quarrel with me, come what might.

News indeed! But after ten if not eleven years of waiting since we first met when she was twenty. Only what had happened? What love affair or affairs had she had that now prompted this liberal approach? Had she changed, given herself to some one? Mayhap she was planning to give herself to me? But I was dubious, and yet in spite of myself curious, too. That old unsatisfied desire to win her! Only now, because of present connections, I almost entirely indifferent emotionally. She had waited too long.

In the meanwhile, I should say, the Freudian interpretation of man's subconscious and its influence on his actions and beliefs had arrived and influenced thought all over America. And curiously, in informing myself concerning it, I had this long while been thinking of Emanuela. Was she not a clear illustration of some of Freud's prime contentions? Her interest in beauty, dancing, sensual art, myself even, her constant flight from sensuality, her peculiarly narrow or conventionalized parents, and very likely her conventionalized if not unhappy youth. What did I know of her really but what she truly desired me to know. The mere fact that she had approached me, however evasively, spelled what? And now this letter. A last despairing effort, maybe. Should I or should I not go? The old lure. Yet by now was I not companionated with one who in every way, artistically and physically, allured, entertained and satisfied me? Only just now she was not here; had taken "stock" work in Cleveland. And in a week or so I was planning to go there in order to be with her. But this now? Did I not owe it to myself as a psychologist and writer?

On the train I calmly speculated as to the possible inroads of time in Emanuela's case. When last we met it had seemed to me that one could see that she was eight

years older than when she was nineteen. Yet attractive
enough to bring on that quarrel, as I also recalled. But
now, with two more years added! I climbed down from
the train at Blauvelt and there she was, in a little dog
cart borrowed from a neighbor. But now much more
mature physically, as I could see, something of that old
lissome, lily-like grace absent. But charming as a
woman of twenty-nine can be. The most attractive
literary woman I had ever seen, I thought. But still
enamored, as I soon found, of all those purely mental
things which are the arts and which reflect rather than
are life. But were we likely to quarrel again because
of that? Not I. If she chose to be more amenable, less
remote and evasive, well and good—I would escape
her, maybe. We should see. But did I honestly want
her now? Time had changed her too much from the
nineteen-year-old beauty I had admired. Oh, well, life
was like that. Why kick? Besides, I was so differently
placed emotionally now than when we had last met.
So much more contented and gay.

And my being so minded, maybe, we got along better than ever before. Certainly she was now more
friendly and companionable than ever she had been,
and I had agreed with myself that I was not going to
argue with her about anything, especially herself. Poof!
We certainly should be able to differ now without
fighting. I certainly had never accepted her viewpoint
and decidedly she had not accepted mine. But to-day it
really made no difference. And yet, as I noticed now,

her words, whatever the topic, were less emphatic or defiant. Unquestionably, she had begun to compromise, in my case at least. But why? Had she read my most recent book and liked it? Had she begun to conceive more kindly of me? Did all men, because of her learned and dogmatic attitude, now shun her? I looked at the swinging body in the white, fleecy dress as she walked from one local shop to another purchasing supplies for the week-end, and could not believe it.

"Tell me, Emanuela," I asked at one point, and curious as to the effect of the question upon her, "have you been interested by this Freudian wave that has swept over us all? And do you accept it as the solution of all that is claimed for it?"

Oh, yes, she had read Freud, and had been impressed in part, but could not accept him fully. No. His analysis was too coarse and too domineering, left no place for anything but itself. And there was nothing that was the whole truth about anything. Still, it had been a revelation to her. But sex the base of *all* dreams? She was by no means sure that she agreed with that. In fact, she was sure she did not. For how offensive to find that life flourished above such muddy depths, had its roots sunk in them as he seemed to think! It certainly was disagreeable.

Followed a long talk on chemistry and physics—the physics of Jacques Loeb, the chemistry of Metchnikoff and Crookes and Curie and Le Bel and Carrel and whom not else, whose revelations in regard to the functions and activities of light and the glands were already puzzling the thinking world. For the first time in connection with her, having read widely since first we had met, I understood her better, could see a great many of the parental as well as midwestern American social conceptions actively operative in her. In spite of all her studies and her desire to know, she was, as she would have put it, "clean-minded," or as I would have phrased it, not quite broad enough (in spite of all her yearnings toward wisdom) to feel or believe that there is an understanding which makes all things clean—a sufficiently great understanding. Wheaton; her youth in a reserved girls' school; her guarded investigations at one of our alleged universities; her connections with popular and respectable magazines, authors, publishers, investigators even! I felt them all in her, working or congealed and binding.

And despite a broadened liking for me, as indicated by little nuances of tone and manner, I was still—if not as much as of old—irritated by the truth that in the face of all she knew—at thirty or thirty-one years of age—she was still hesitating before or whimpering over the scandal of procreation. "Offensive that life should flourish above muddy depths!" What rot! Depths indeed! And this in the face of all her beauty and seeming fitness for the very thing which she abhorred.

And not only that, but sensing as I did at the time that I received her invitation (as well as here in actual contact with her), that she brought me here in connection with some fight with herself—some battle between her sensual and her puritanic natures—I was irritated to find myself being made use of in this way. For hours after I arrived, as we went about the town or afterwards drove out to her charming studio, I looked at her suspiciously and I must say with a great deal of secret criticism. So beautiful and yet so strange. Crazy, really. All but frozen forever in her conventions and recessions. Yet compelled just the same, but by her mind and not her body or emotions, to take up with a man like myself and one to whom for years, on mental and moral grounds, she had objected, and from whom too often she had fled in a kind of defensive hate or disgust. Oh, Lord! But now at last daring to invite me to visit her in this semi-secluded place. But for what? Would she admit it to herself even now?

But as she soon indicated, her maidenly precautions had prevailed even in such a pseudo-liberal world as this. Sigrid, her maid, she explained, was well known in this colony for her religious convictions. More, she had told the woman who owned the place and leased it to the artists—the one, by the way, to whom the handsome dog cart belonged—that I was to occupy the tent down among the birches—a tent, by the way, that for several summers past had been occupied by a well-known painter. And not only that, but this evening as well as on the morrow in the late afternoon, several friends were stopping in for tea and dinner. (How careful, I thought, as she named them.) But I need not and would not be bothered by that, since I should not be staying long. This hopeless creature, I finally thought to myself. Why should I not turn around now and take the next train back?

But having come so far and noting the exquisite charm of the place, I decided not. I was working on some sketches of men and had one with me. More, the tent faced one of the loveliest stony brooks I have ever seen, and extending from one side overlooking the brook was a brown sail awning, underneath which, on a smooth lawn, were a table and chair. Inside on a shelf were a number of interesting books. Up from the field which surrounded the house rose the slope of a great hill, green and cool in the late afternoon, and with clumps of shadowy black pines alternating with enormous bowlders and patches of perfect greensward. No, I would stay. She might think as she pleased, go where she pleased, act as she pleased. So long as I received my meals promptly, here I would stick, until Monday or Tuesday, anyhow. It was hot in town. And as for her and her friends, why not cut them? Unquestionably, in some errant, repressed and nervous way, she was thinking that I would assail and overcome her, cave-man fashion, and so free her once and for all of her long and possibly,—how should I know— torturing self-restraint—slay the dragon of repression that shut the Sleeping Princess from the world of her fancy. Well, no dragon would be slain by me this trip. She was going to be allowed to sleep on, now and forever as far as I was concerned.

And so I announced that I would prefer to avoid her guests and have my dinner here beside the tent. Also my breakfast. And that on the morrow I would decide as to what else. The place moved me to work, inspired me. And I began examining the books on the shelves resting on birch stakes driven into the ground, also a fishing rod which stood in one corner. But though I thought to be rid of her in this fashion, I was wrong. The guests, as she explained, were not coming until five or five-thirty, and it was now only three. We could walk along the shore of this brook and investigate a rugged gorge which in ages past had cut its way. And this we did. Only before doing so it was necessary for her to return to the studio some two hundred yards away and leave instructions for Sigrid. And this she did. But not without, as I noticed on her return, changing her costume. The summery things in which she had met me were replaced now by an ensemble more suitable to a ramble —a rough tweed skirt and bright jumper and cap.

And so an hour or two in which we seemed to relax and she to give herself over to dreams, regardless of whether my intentions or philosophy agreed with hers or not. Had I noticed one thing in connection with bees? She had not before this summer. There was balsam growing wild farther down the stream here, and evidently its honey was of a more desirable kind than most, for the bees were legion and loud in their efforts to secure it. And alas, as unrestrained and as dissolute as men in their search for an intoxicant. For,— and I might believe it or not as I wished, daily at about this time or earlier one could find scores of them on their backs on the ground under the lovely pink bells which carried this sweet, too full of honey or its alcoholic content to fly on their way. I laughed, and went with her to see them. But thinking the while that her old-fashioned Puritanism was certainly being contended with, for she would not have talked of such a subject with me six years before. Nor the next one either, which concerned a girl whom we encountered crossing a little log-rail bridge which spanned this brook farther up. This was obviously an ignorant but not unattractive girl, whose clothes were the flags of her disposition—too bright, too emphatic, and she herself too forward and rakish in her stride and glances. I could not help meditating on the reckless chemistry of youth and ignorance. But as she drew near Emanuela began with: "Look! I'll tell you about her afterward." Then nodding to her as she passed and receiving a friendly "How-do" in return, she turned to me with: "She's the daughter of Mrs. Pringle, a woman who does most of the washing and ironing around here. They're very poor and this girl is supposed to work in New York. She only comes home week-ends occasionally. The pathetic part of it is that it's so obvious what she is, and that her mother doesn't know anything about her, for she talks of her daughter's success in New York." As a matter of fact, the girl comes out here to meet certain people and her mother doesn't even know that."

"Ruined!" I commented. "A hopelessly bad girl."

"Oh, yes"—and I rather marveled, I must say, at Emanuela's soft uncritical "Oh, yes," as well as her free and easy discussion of this decidedly unconventional situation. For formerly she would not have discussed any such thing. But now she added, and in a quite understanding way, as I thought, "But it is a little sad, I think. I feel so sorry for her ignorant hardworking mother as well as her. She never had a real opportunity."

"Oh, I don't know," I argued. "If they don't know any better, and find any real satisfaction, who's hurt or really unhappy?"

For answer she looked at me, yet said nothing—a queer and even developed or maybe, as she might see it, defeated change in her.

But coming from Emanuela it was interesting. Never before had she given me any evidence of understanding of, let alone sympathy with such people in their profound incompetence and inconsequence. Or with immorality, either. Could it be that she was trying to prove to me that she had changed, was no longer the critical Minerva that I had known?

Yet all of this now fell on dubious and even unsympathetic ears. For I was by no means satisfied that Emanuela was more than trifling or flirting with danger. No doubt she felt that her state was peculiar; that by reason of her views or her peculiar unresponsiveness she was or had been allowing her glorious youth to pass into the sere and yellow without quite thinking or knowing what she was doing. But even so, and in spite of her present mood in regard to herself, there were, no doubt, still deep-seated, strong inhibitions in her which would save her. I was sure of it, Freud or no Freud, age or no age. And so I was inclined to take her and her present mood with a grain of salt. Let her rest, or let her worry. True, up to a year or two or three before I had grieved over her not a little. But now I was no longer so interested. For what was the real truth about her? Could she really love me or any one? Nonsense! I would not believe it. And I would not be first or last aid to some one who was concluding that her youth was being wasted. The thought was chilling.

Still here was the lovely afternoon sun streaming down the hillside. And here Emanuela like some bright orchid wandering over this lovely grass with me. What a crazy thing this living and loving could turn out to be! And what a pity that like all the other contacts, this was destined to be a failure too—only not because of her but because of me.

Sensing that I was indifferent (I assume), she now truly devoted herself to me. And it is true that I relented and went to dinner at the studio, but left early.

But afterwards, at ten-thirty, she came down to see whether I knew how to tuck myself in comfortably and warmly for the night. Did I understand this tent cot and the mosquito net contrivance that went with it? There appeared to be some mystery concerning tucking oneself in which I was not supposed to understand and which perhaps, once I had worked myself in for the night, she might return and make sure about. But ah, Emanuela, I thought, the obviousness of all this! Truly, you must be innately lacking in the fever which makes for mating, for I cannot feel even a trace of that which apparently should be moving you. And sex is not a thought but an emotion. It comes upon one like heat or weakness. This something which is now moving you must be what—an idea merely, a thin, foggily tinted thought, I am sure, which has nothing in common with the ordinary and yet so lovely sensuality which sways the flesh. Or am I misreading you, and are you really moved by something which I cannot feel?

So troubled and puzzled was I by these thoughts that I could not extract any real romance from this situation. Not a trace. I could not feel the glow which I had always anticipated would accompany such a situation as this. Damn! Double-damn! And in such an exquisite world—the moon shining outside, this sparkling stream! I was so cross that by the time she did return, clothed in a soft, thin cape and looking sylphlike in the moonlight, I was frankly determined to indicate my indifference. Why not? She had never hesitated to indicate her indifference to me.

She came over to where I was lying on my side looking out through the lifted tent-flap at the stream and pretending not to see her. But now . . . and if you will believe it . . . a sudden and all but inexplainable change of heart or mood. The moon on her face. The moon-stippled stream outside, trilling and bubbling over the rocks and pebbles.

"All comfy?" she asked.

She was making sure that the blankets about my feet were snugly tucked in. I rose on my elbow and looked at her.

"Yes, very."

"You managed to find out how it is done?"

"Well, you might revise the work for me."

She came close to the head of the cot. And then, in the face of my earlier thoughts, I seized her tight and pulled her close to me, sure at last that all her earlier resistance had passed. Yet now, when I sought to draw her face to mine, her body in with me, there was a sudden outburst of that old and seemingly mentally uncontrolled or psychically automatic resistance which had so painfully amazed me in the past and which appeared to leave her powerless to do otherwise. It consisted if of anything of an automatic chemic and so vital rejection, which finally resulted in her releasing herself and running, her cape which had come off in the struggle remain-

ing in my hands. But with none of the sharp commands or protests which previously, and much to my
irritation, had always met my approaches. Instead,
principally silence, at best a low muttered "Don't,
please." And perhaps, as I thought afterward, more
genuine physical, and so uncontrollable, fear than
mental opposition as before.

But just the same, and because of all my previous
thoughts, I was now determined to let her go. I had
not really intended to seize her, and if at this late date,
and after all these obviously thought-out preparations
she could contest in this manner, let her remain as she
was! Certainly there was no real romance or inspiration in it for me. And with that, turning over in my
tousled cot and sleeping soundly, so soundly indeed
as to be awakened only by the morning sun pouring
through the fly which had been raised for the night.
And no Emanuela. Later and after I had concealed
the cape, Sigrid arrived with the matutinal bacon,
eggs and coffee.

But at ten, and just as I was about to go for a walk,
Emanuela. But with no suggestion in her manner or
her eyes of the nervous and flighty contest of the night
before. On the contrary, a genial assumption of its
non-occurrence. Wasn't it a glorious day? Had I slept
well? (I assured her I had slept perfectly.) Well, then,
if I were agreeable and wasn't too angry with her, she
would suggest that we have a swim. Only about a mile
away there was a lovely granite pool which, hewed out

of solid rock and fed by a tumbling rill, was a part of
the estate of Mr. and Mrs. Somebody now in Europe
for the summer. It had been designed and cut out of
the solid rock by the late Stanford White, who was a
friend of the mistress of the place. She could get me a
bathing suit that belonged to somebody here.

On my signifying my willingness she was off,
only to return presently with two suits. And together we walked, but with no word concerning anything or any one, just the beauties of this estate we were
crossing. I should see how lovely it all was. Yet all the
while I was going over her, in a psychopathic sense,
with a fine-toothed comb. Impossible. This pendulum-
like swinging between desire and revulsion now puzzled as much as it irritated me. For here she was
proposing a bath—which meant her tempting figure
in a bathing suit, and us two alone together. Yet judg-
ing by her expression, no consciousness of all this,—
neither of me nor any other man as her lover or
courtier. A dozen times I was on the verge of speaking,
breaking forth, really, but decided not to. Let me see
if she would manage to dismiss all this without a word.

And so, presently, the pool. A great basin of water,
entirely encircled by trees and with bath cabinets directly beyond the northern edge of the rock. Non-
chalantly enough she took the bundle of suits and tow-
els which I had been carrying and opened and divided
the contents.

But her eyes! Her face! You could not possibly

have gathered from either that the romance of the
scene or the possibility of a sensual reëncounter with
me was moving or troubling her in any way. As a
matter of fact, and as always, a renewed sense of emotional chill or wall of reserve, which I now believe
was involuntary and constructed of unnamable and
uncontrollable fears or doubts which, like the doors of
the water-tight compartment of a ship, and always
in the face of danger or assumed danger, roll to, shut-
ting all within safe from harm without—in her case
the flood of harm that her soul most desired.

I was first out of the bath-house and waiting. And
beautiful certainly she was when she appeared in her
two-piece apple-green suit, all the more provoking,
maybe, because of her eternal elusiveness. At once she
dived into the water and came up to a rock ledge on the
opposite side, calling to me to emulate her. Delib-
erately I studied all the graceful lines of her, but still
with the chill of her own self-protective determination
upon me. Why dive in or come to her? Did I not
know how it would result? Evasions and a quarrel.
Yet if I wished to quarrel now, as I did, I must do
something to provoke a quarrel. So plunging in and
coming up beside her, I slipped my arms about
her and pulled her down to me, holding her close
the while I pressed my lips to her neck. But only,
as I had anticipated, to again encounter a vigorous muscular rejection. I couldn't and shouldn't. I can still hear
the commonplace and lying or frightened "Listen!

Please, you mustn't! I won't have this! Surely you don't think it was for anything like this that I brought you to such a public place as this!"

"But you listen to me, instead, Emanuela." I now began. "For you're talking to me for the last time. And that's final. I'm going back to New York after dinner, and you're not going to see me any more, here or anywhere, I promise you. You've played with me for the last time. Last night when you came down to me I thought you had at last decided to face this thing and do what you really want to do. And that was the only reason I took hold of you, and for no other, because I had decided that at last you did know what you wanted and were willing to admit it. Up to that time I was certain that you did not. And I did not run after you because I did not want to, because I was sure that as usual you did not know your own mind. And the same way to-day when you came around with your plans. I came along not because I really expected you would do anything with me or anybody, Emanuela, because I know you won't. You're afraid. You're the victim of some Freudian twist which you can't overcome, and that's the truth! There's something wrong with you. You're suffering from an inhibition of some kind against sex, your normal relationship to men and life. Yet you have been hoping that I, or somebody—but not because you really care for me or any one—would help you realize yourself in spite of yourself. And yet whenever I have tried to help you, look what has happened! Last night, for instance. That time I came to your place on the East Side. And to-day, right here. I think you must be mad. In fact, I'm sure you are. You're always playing around near the thing you want, and yet when it's really offered to you, you pretend to yourself and to me that you don't want it."

"Oh, please, hush. You don't understand me at all," she exclaimed.

"Oh, don't I? Well, have it that way if you wish. Only this time I'm going."

And I swam across the pool and so out to my dressing room. And after me Emanuela, I suppose, for when I came out dressed again she was there waiting. But a little repressed or depressed, I cannot say which. And together we went along the path, resuming the discussion as before, but without bitterness now, really with great philosophic calm. And finally Emanuela saying to me: "Oh well, you may be right. I don't know. I'm not going to try to explain or adjust myself now. All I know is that I feel as I do and I don't propose to do anything that I don't feel strongly moved to do."

"Right!" I said, and maybe a little more viciously than was necessary. "But then you shouldn't trouble to try to move people to do things that they are not aching to do, either."

"That may be true. I guess it is. But oh, how cruel you can be!" she suddenly exclaimed, her eyes narrowing and her lips twitching in a troubled and nervous way.

We walked in silence to the studio.

I could catch a six-thirty train to New York as I found, and so threw my few things into a bag. And still courteously accompanied by Emanuela, who could at all times maintain the most diplomatic and reserved demeanor even in the face of such a fiasco as this, was driven by her to the station. And as the train pulled out there she was, waving a smiling farewell.

And then silence—another four years without a word. And then (such is the binding power of old contacts) a letter. As always it carried the easy, familiar tone of one old friend to another. To be sure, we had had our usual spat when we last met, and no one had regretted it more than had she afterwards. But she would not revive any anger for the world. And she would have been in touch with me long before this only there had been serious interfering things. For one thing, not six months after I had seen her, her mother had fallen ill again and she had spent over six months with her traveling and nursing her. And after that—and only in the last six months—a truly greater calamity had befallen her. For her father, for whom she had always entertained a genuine affection, had suffered a stroke of paralysis, and was, she feared, permanently done with his hitherto active life. And it was all so sad, for he did not want to be. Worse, she was now finding both of her parents more or less dependent on her, not wishing to be separated from her. Yet, too, she could not afford to be permanently dissevered from New York either, and on that account she had at last succeeded in inducing her mother to sell the place in Wheaton and buy a comfortable place on the Hudson, near New York, where she would be in touch with things that interested her and where her friends could come. And here they all had been since the previous spring.

But would I not like to come up? It was so beautiful there. Every convenience, a lovely view, and they had a car. And it was the real purpose of this letter to ask me. Her father and mother had a separate wing to themselves and that left her almost an entire house in which to entertain. And while she had been able to reassemble at least some of her old connections, still the one person she would really enjoy having with her from time to time would be me. I could come and stay and work there as much and as long as I pleased —for the summer, if I chose, and the winter, too. For there were rooms to spare. And I need not fear any of the old scenes any more, for she had changed considerably. It was now an honest and warm friendship she was offering, one based on our long and, certainly on her part at least, honestly sympathetic relationship. Only I had never really believed so. Yet if she had acted strangely in my eyes, never had she been wanting in a real and hearty liking for me. And I must not judge her too harshly. Perhaps my judgment of her had been right. She had often thought so since. But certainly there was no ulterior motive now. I must believe that. And would I not come?

I pondered over this letter and decided after a time that I would not go but would merely write and thank her for the invitation. But before I troubled to do this, I was confronted by her once more. It was a cold, rainy, dark November afternoon. And she arrived at my door, hooded and cloaked in a blue rubber rain coat and cap, with gloves and umbrella to match. But looking—to put it in the mildest form— changed. For although stouter and apparently vigorous and healthy, yet even in the somber light of my studio I could see that her skin was not as fresh as when I had last seen her, nor her eyes as lustrous, nor had she that old swinging, buoyant stride that had characterized her. Otherwise, apparently well enough.

And how had I been? I had not answered her, had I? But surely we were still good enough friends. I assured her smilingly that we were. And then more talk about the house, although I felt that that had really nothing to do with her visit. Then once her things were off, she threw herself into a large chair before the open fire and gazed at it, her elbow resting on one arm of the chair, her chin in the palm of her hand. She was more quiet and thoughtful than ever I had seen her, less erect and defiant or assured.

"Life doesn't do as much to you as to some, does it?"

she finally ventured, looking at me. "Yet you have had plenty to contend with, too. I know that." Then she paused again. "But you have a lot of strength to face it with."

"And that's very cheering," I added, cynically.

"Well, it's better than not having it, anyhow." And then she gazed into the fire again. I could see that not a little was wrong.

"What's the matter, Emanuela?" I finally said. "I know you have come to tell me something. What is it?"

"Oh, if you really must know, it's my life. I hardly know where to begin. It seems to me as though for all my living I haven't really lived; as though just now, or in the last two or three years at any rate, I have been seeing things as they are. And it hasn't been very pleasant for me. Oh, I know what you'll say— that it's my own fault and that it could have been different. And perhaps it could have been—if I had been different. Yes, I know it could have been. But how is one to be different if one isn't?"

She looked at me as though I were likely to answer the question in some new way. "Are you coming to me to ask me that?" I said.

"Oh, no. You know that's not it either. I'm lonely and depressed to-day, that's all."

"But is that really all, Emanuela?"

"Well, no, it isn't either," she finally added and with considerable emphasis—something poignant in her tone, as I thought. "It's something else, and I've been wanting to tell you for a long time. For you're almost the only person I know to whom I can come and who will help me, maybe. It's about my father and mother, you know. I wrote you he had a paralytic stroke. But I didn't tell you all, because I thought . . . oh, well—"

"Well," I interpolated, to encourage her since she had paused.

"Well . . . you know how I have always been," she went on. "But I must tell you now. I really must. I can't stand up against it alone. He,—he—my father, you know, he wanted to leave my mother long ago. They never really understood each other, I suppose, but felt they ought to make the best of it for my sake. And I thought so, too, up to a few years ago. But after that last talk of ours and after he broke down I began to see something. I think now that maybe it was because he didn't leave her or she him—that he had that stroke. It was that that brought it on, I think. And mother's sickness, too, before that. He went off to a hotel once for a month, until there were rumors and until I went out there and induced him to come back for my sake. That was just before I went abroad with her for two years, that time, you know. And he stayed in Chicago. But before we left he told me then that he didn't care for mother and hadn't for a long time past; couldn't endure the monotony of it all, especially after I had gone; that there had never been anything much mentally between him and my mother, and that it was only because of our connections in Chicago and Wheaton and his law practice and his consideration for me that . . . oh, well . . . you know, the usual stuff."

"Yes, I know, Emanuela," I said.

"But that was when I first began to see how things were—how life really is. And besides, I had been reading so much—Freud and psychoanalysis, and thinking of you."

"Well, and then what?"

"Yes, but this is the hardest part, the thing that I suffer most from. It's since he had the stroke, you know. Oh, dear, I sometimes think I am a complete mistake. You were right. I am sure now."

"Go on, Emanuela. Don't be taking the crimes of life upon your shoulders."

"But if I hadn't persuaded him to come back. If I hadn't talked in my usual way, argued that it could be endured by him and her for all our sakes."

"Yes, I know."

"Why then, you see, he might not have had the stroke . . . maybe he might not . . . and then . . ."

She stopped talking and putting her chin in both hands, lowered her head and turned away from me.

"Listen, Emanuela," I said. "It doesn't follow at all that he would not have. Besides, you have faced life well enough until now. Let's see you face it now. Tell me the rest, whatever it is."

"But, oh dear." (She brushed something away from

her eyes.) "It's so dreadful. You see mother hasn't told any one, doesn't want any one to know. But he's no longer right in his mind. And now, well, this is the dreadful part of it, all he thinks of, all he wants to do is to kill her. Isn't that dreadful? He's lame, you know, now, and he can't lift his arms above the elbows so he can't hurt any one. But all the time, all the time, night and day, when he thinks she is around anywhere, he comes slipping. I can always tell by the shuffling of his feet. He can't walk—he can only shuffle his feet. And she can always hear him beforehand—coming, you know—in the night or any time—but most always at night. (Her face was tense and drawn as she said this.) And sometimes he has a knife, or sometimes it's a stick of wood or a piece of iron, or anything. Once it was a chair. But to hear him slipping about in the night like that, after we've gone to bed, shuffling along in the dark, trying the doors or fumbling at the locks! Oh, it's terrible! It's dreadful. And all the worse because I know now why, even if mother doesn't. She still doesn't understand—believes that everything has been done just right. Oh, dear, it's always so easy to take whatever he has away from him and make him go back to bed. But we can always hear him. And we have to watch, too, because he might do something, you know, invent some way. And mother cries so, although even now she doesn't understand."

For a moment or two I sat and gazed at her. What

a dénouement! And for her. Actually I was sorry, very.

"Sex repression, Emanuela," I added. "Long years of it. You see for yourself, don't you?"

"Oh, yes, I see. I know now. You needn't tell me. But it's so dreadful to have him there that way. And yet mother feels that it is so dreadful to send him away. And I do, too. I have always cared for him so much."

"And so because of what you think people may say or find out . . . Oh, Emanuela, for God's sake, do come to! Wake up! Don't track along in the beaten path to the grave. Think for yourself. Act according to your real right-now emotions. Surely you and your mother, because of your ridiculous Illinois notions and connections, are not going to torture yourselves in this way. For heaven's sake! Put him in an asylum. Take your mother and travel. Get out and away. You have the means. And don't come here and cry. It's too impossible! And you talk of reading Freud and seeing life in a new way!"

"But I've pleaded with mother to do that very thing. I know it's sad. But still . . ."

"And what would you like me to do? Come up and call a physician and have the situation cleared up for you? There's no other way, you know. Why the deuce can't you act—a hell like that because of what people will think, for you know that's the really chief part of all this. What you or your mother will personally suffer at seeing him properly cared for somewhere else is neither here nor there in this case. You know he will be better off away from you than with you. And so will you two be away from him. And yet here you sit and cry!" I got up, thoroughly irritated.

"Oh, yes, I see it all clear enough. But I have been in such a state. Mother is really ill herself now. I did so want to talk to you before of this. Yes, I will do as you say, of course. I know it can't be helped. But I did want to talk it over with you. You don't mind, do you?"

"Mind? Of course not. But what a genius you have for doing the conventional thing, Emanuela, and making me want to beat you up into the bargain!"

She smiled sadly. She did wish I would come up. And that time—did I remember? I was right, and she was wrong. I should have forced her. But would I come up just for old sake's sake? It would do them both so much good.

And I did go, once.

But the week following her father was taken away, and about three months later died. Then two years after she wrote me that her mother had died. Still later, perhaps as much as six months, she wrote asking if she could come to see me. I replied "Of course." This time, as it seemed to me, she looked much older—had changed more than in any interval in which she had been away from me. Her face and body were fuller and heavier, more matronly. Not only that, but in her face was a trace of something—could it be a shadow of grossness?—her repressed emotions or desires at last gaining headway? I thought so. But also a sagging resignation which seemed to bode no good for herself—little of the self-confidence which had characterized all of her earlier years.

After a few commonplaces concerning what she had been doing, she came to the meat of her visit—*what to do with her life*. Truly, as she said, she was in a bad way. Her life had all but gone to pieces. Not that she didn't have means or couldn't write—the kind of thing she had always written. But somehow, after her recent experience, that type of thing did not seem so truly representative. (I smiled inwardly but said nothing.) And she hadn't sufficiently found herself in any new way to picture a new type of thing. (I wanted to say: "Emanuela, you have never really expressed yourself as a woman, and so you do not know men and women or life." But I did not say it.) But what was she to do with herself? That was her problem. How to connect up with life? And since I had aided her once before, she had come back. "You see, you have so many connections. You see life from so many sides. Perhaps you will see what is the matter with me or where I can fit in."

But actually, as I looked at her now, I could not see that anything was to be done. It was too late. She had never functioned properly as a woman, had never seen life clearly. Not only that, but even now, and in spite of her father's and mother's ends and her own sensual and mental defeat, I doubted if she fully grasped her lacks or what they had cost her. Plain it was that there was or had been something missing in her from the very start—no clear vision. But at any rate, why talk of writing or connecting up with life at this late day and when the beauty and the appeal which had made it all so possible had all but vanished?

For a moment I was moved by a desire to make an additional verbal or mental attack—to take a final vengeful fling in repayment for all my futile efforts to reach her. But then I thought, why? And how cruel, when she was so low in her mood. It was true that throughout the years, and in the face of my various statements to myself and her, I had really wanted to share her life—so much so in those first years— but now. . . ! And through me or herself in relation to me or some other—Scheib, say—it might have come about that she would have better understood life, acquired that grip on reality which would have vitalized the literary or narrative gift that she had. But was that true, either? Could she ever have been any real thing? I doubted it now.

At last I had resort to the old prescription about work being the cure for every ill. She was by no means through as yet. She must not think so. It was too ridiculous. Twenty more good years, at least. Besides, she was so much wiser now. Experience had broad-

ened her in so many ways, and it was foolish to say
that she could not interpret life from this new angle.
She had the narrative ability. And once she did, would
she not find herself—as her own experience in connection with her earlier writings had proved—in touch
with those who would understand and appreciate her
new point of view? And would not that compensate
and be connecting up with life, as much as any one
could reasonably expect to be connected up with it?

She listened, but I am sure she sensed insincerity
or perhaps indifference in what I said. At any rate,
after a time she got up, and adjusting her scarf, exclaimed: "Oh, what's the use of life, anyhow? I used
to think I understood what it was about, but now I
know I don't. And I'm indifferent or not suited to it
any more, I guess. I should have married or given
myself to you. I know that now, but just knowing
what life is really like now doesn't help me. It's too
late, I guess."

She did not appear to be looking for additional comments or sympathy, and I did not venture to offer
any. As she went out she said: "But I do wish you
would come to see me some time. I've sold the place
up there and am down here now," and she gave me
her address. And I assured her: "Yes, certainly!"

But from that day to this I have never seen nor
heard of Emanuela. It may be that she is dead—although I doubt it.

ESTHER NORN

Esther Norn

Somehow, when I think of her I think always of a girl of nineteen or twenty, with bright red hair, a face of strong and yet sensitive lines, and much beauty though always pale, and a figure such as most women might envy. In fact, when I first knew her she seemed to have a debonair Scotch presence and manner, as though she were one of those lassies whom Burns had in mind when he wrote, "Green Grow the Rashes, O," but this was more of an appearance than a reality. I believe that she was of Irish extraction, on her father's side anyhow.

Like most girls of her years she was markedly conscious of her beauty and that something about her which made her know that she had a strong appeal for men, although she made no particularly disturbing use of it. She knew, too, that she had a Scotch look and air whether she was from Scotland or not, and that that had an appeal for some. To emphasize this she affected usually a tam-o'-shanter, a Scotch plaid for a throw or a skirt, and shoes if not stockings that had a sturdy, open-air look about them.

There is such a thing as knowing too much about this business of living. One can sense, let us say, even though one is but a girl of eighteen or twenty, that life is a crass and hit-or-miss game, that the race is not always to the swift or the strong or the beautiful, but that time and chance happen to all men and that in the main the maker of life is too strong, too clever and too remorseless for the sons of men. You may guess, say, at seventeen or eighteen, if not earlier, more especially if you chance to be a woman and see how very much in vain some men battle for beauty and some women for love, that men are forever launching little cockleshell craft upon a limitless and troubled sea that come to nowhere, faring forth early in search of some rumored and mysterious Atlantis, the blessed isles of happiness, and never finding them. I know that Esther Norn thought of all these things at nineteen and twenty, and later came to think even more darkly of life though always, curious as it may seem to some, cheerfully. She was always smiling, always ready to discuss any passing adventure or to enter upon it as though it were interesting. I have discussed many such things with her and am convinced that she was well aware of the fact that by some mischance she was born under circumstances that were unfavorable to the best development of herself and her beauty. Her mother had died early and she had been brought up by her father, a somber, lymphatic, imperfect man who made his living betimes and between much drinking and pursuing of women (to whom he was not very attractive) as a sales clerk and on occasion a floorwalker. In fact, he was one of those men about whom one finds it difficult to say anything, a sort of nonentity with nevertheless a number of destructive vices.

What Esther Norn thought of him I often wondered, for for the most part she would never discuss him. Yet he was about and at one time and another, apparently, dependent upon her. Quite frequently he was out of work.

When I first knew her they were living in one of those narrow, dingy, colorless, ill-lighted, musty flats that used to line both sides of what is now Park Avenue, then as pointless and colorless a thoroughfare as any in New York. For years and years before this, so I learned, her father had found it difficult to sustain either his wife or his daughter in the necessaries of life. At the time I met her she was serving as a counter clerk or cashier in a small laundry in that immediate vicinity, although she was already interesting herself in the stage as a prospect and was a twice-a-week instructor in a small dancehall. But there had already developed a slight weakness of the heart which warned her to guard herself against too strenuous exercise.

Apart from this and a somewhat nebulous and dreamy temperament, it was easy to see that her father was her greatest handicap. So often he was out of work, and at that time she was under the impression that it was her moral duty to stand by him and make as much of a home for him as she could. It was certainly not much of a home, for neither at that time nor later was she given to interest herself in things relating to the home. The few times I saw her and her father there she seemed to me as one who was living in a dream and who, for that reason perhaps, sensed not too sharply the dreary nature of the life around her.

As it chanced though, I saw nothing more of her for several years, (being but a casual visitor in company with one who was much interested in her), and yet during that time I heard not a little concerning her. Poor Esther. Her father was *so* worthless. And here she was, living up in that dark little flat with no one to do anything for her and working all the time to help a father who would never be of the least service to her, who would pull her down really. Now and again I heard that he was drinking, that recently he had lost his place at Stern's or somewhere else, (which same he had only a little while before secured), that she was trying to get on the stage, that she liked and read the most interesting books, that her views were unusual and illuminating, and so on and so forth. Because of these things I could never quite get her out of my mind, the quaint picture of youth in poverty, a kind of other-worldliness which she presented in her dingy little flat.

And then after a time I learned from this same friend that she had obtained a very small part in a play—a maid announcing some one, I think. Later I heard that, like so many others, she had found stage work very uncertain as to continuity and to bridge over one period and another of non-employment was working as waitress in a very polite and artistic little restaurant in upper Madison Avenue, the proprietress of which had taken a fancy to her. Next, having moved into Tenth Street (Greenwich Village), I heard of her there as friend and companion of two girls who were conducting a knickknack art shop for the benefit of the curious and gullible who were already beginning to nose about this area. Then I was told that she had fallen in love with a rich young man, part artist, part loafer, part globe-trotter and part writer, a person of very fascinating ways who came and went, here and there, in search of pleasure and things to interest him. For a year I heard nothing more as to this. It seems that he had an apartment or bachelor quarters on the borders of Greenwich Village with which she was in some morganatic way—I would not venture to say just how—connected. They were presumed to be in love, I believe. After something over a year of this I heard that he had gone again, Esther remaining in what mood I cannot guess. At that time she and her father were living—or at least her father was—in some even worse rooms in the upper Forties near Third Avenue. During this year she had been in a play or two, but they had lasted only a little while. I heard that her heart trouble was chronic and irremediable, a weakness of the walls which would not permit her to pursue dancing or to take part in any violent physical exercise but which should not keep her from the stage or at least rôles that were not too strenuous. With such a heart I wondered how ultimately she would make out.

Thereafter I noticed her about the Village, gradually, it seemed to me, becoming a fixture there. How she lived I could not guess. Meeting her on the street one bitter January day and noticing that she was not any too warmly dressed, I reminded her that we knew each other and asked her: "Why not stop in and warm up for a moment? There are two coal fires going in my fireplaces." Without a word she turned and accompanied me. She found a white wool rug and sat down cross-legged before one of the fires. I think she remained there for over an hour, scarcely stirring and with scarcely a word to me, neither of us being in any mood for talking. But I noticed how feelingly she dreamed into the fire. She had the poise and the charm of a graven image.

At that time she really did suggest those lassies whom Burns was fond of picturing. Her brow was very white. Her neck had a lovely curve to it. Her hair was such a rich red, and her eyes so blue and still. She was wearing a plaid skirt and a tam-o'-shanter. Now and then, seeing that I had begun to write, she would turn and smile at me, a faint suggestion of a contented smile, as much as to say: "I am very comfortable here and much obliged to you." After an hour she rose, touched her hair slightly before a mirror, and left. When we met thereafter we were friends and occasionally when I met her somewhere alone I would invite her to lunch or dinner. Sometimes—and I always noticed that the thing was done with a clear perception of the friendly and yet curious interest I had in her—she would say: "Why, yes," and wheel and come with me; or, "No, I can't to-day. Sorry." And then, with that faint, friendly and yet elusive and almost mocking Mona Lisa smile, she would go on.

I came, without ever understanding her, to like her very much. And, without ever understanding me, I think she liked me. We could sit and talk about characters in the Village, exhibits, books; and to my pleasure though never to my surprise I found her most definitely and effectively sensitive to all the current moods and theories tied up with the arts and with thought. At this time I gathered that once more she was making some little money by helping occasionally in a restaurant that was artistic and very popular; also that she was already a part of one of the several Little Theater movements then current in the Village and by reason of which she came by a little money—I cannot guess how little. When in the Village, as I rather guessed than knew at this time, she would stop with the two girls of the curio place, and when out of it with her father.

It was about this time, though, that I began to hear of her in connection with an individual whom I had encountered before and whom I had never been quite able to either like or dislike. To me he was a somewhat disorderly blend of the charlatan, the poseur, the congenital eccentric, and the genius, or honest, sincere, seeking thinker, the charlatan, and genius sectors being at times not too clearly discernible. All too often he appeared to me to be an on-the-surface eccentric and clown or court-jester. Self-avowedly a poet and a tramp, he was forever admitting or rather insisting upon the fact that he was a genius. At one time in his career, or so I heard,—and from himself if I am not mistaken—he had worn sandals without socks (this in the dead of winter, too), no undershirt, no underclothing of any kind, a coarse wool or cotton working man's shirt open at the neck, no hat, no tie, and not often an overcoat unless he was flush and could afford one or some one gave him one. But when I met him he had returned to shoes and socks, but still no hat and not often an overcoat. Before either Esther or I knew him he had tramped over a goodly portion of the world, always with the least possible effort on his part, and had finally landed in Greenwich Village, only to be heard of in connection with various eccentric thoughts and deeds. As I saw it, he was suffering from a rabid form of ego-mania which would not permit him to remain quiet anywhere. He must be heard from, either via his costume, his gestures, his speech, or his ideas. Afterward he wrote a book about himself which in a praiseworthy way I must say, set himself forth for what he was; a mixture of the charlatan, the poseur, the genius, and the honest, sincere thinker and on occasion the dunce or fool. At that time I was rather more than less impressed with the thought that he was a dunce and a clown.

Imagine my surprise then when one day, meeting some one who knew most of the gossip of the Village, I learned that Esther Norn had become enamored of this jackanapes poet, as had he of her, and that they had married and gone to live in one of those spare, bare rooms which constituted one phase of the various outstanding aspects of the social life of this region. "Yes," declared my informant, with a look and an air of astonishment, "she is actually in love with him and he with her. Of course I can understand his being crazy about her, but what she sees in him is beyond me."

And sure enough, meeting him on the street one morning, he feeling me to be a friend not only to his bride but to himself, I presume, was most effusive in his picturing of his present bliss. He had met her at a party. She had looked exactly like a mediæval Madonna—which in truth she did at times. He had fallen wildly, madly, irrevocably in love with her. Instantly he had rushed home to compose a poem, or many poems, to her, and had rushed back to read them to her there and then. In fact he had dogged her steps and pleaded with her until she had consented to listen to him. For in her, he insisted, he recognized the one woman who could inspire him to the deeds and the verse that were to make of him a great poet. . . . And all the time his thin jean trousers were chillily flapping against his spare muscular legs. And his shoes, homely and shineless, looked so very trampy. And his hair, long and unkempt, blew about his face. And his rough hands were by no means immaculate. "The wonder!" I thought. "The strangeness of this thing! I can't believe it." And yet somehow I could not help thinking that it was not so horribly amiss that she should have interested herself in him, after all. He was different and arresting, even though eccentric and somewhat eerie. No doubt she detected merits and charms in him which I did not. "The lucky dog," I thought. "This faun has interested an ancient nymph or wood-sprite. This Panling before me in this gray frieze shirt and belted trousers, without coat or hat, may be a better thing than I am, one of the earlier natural figures of the world." One might almost see horns sprouting from his temples. I could very well guess how he had assaulted her ears with his poetic outpourings, the wild maundering pleas he must have made.

To top all this came the statement that he was now writing better poetry than ever he had. Also more. And forthwith he extracted from one of his pockets an ode which, in the chill winter wind and without an overcoat, he proceeded to read to me there in the street. Zounds! And yet it was not bad. And he added that *The Independent* had accepted and was about to publish two poems which he had been able to write because of her, also that *The Outlook* and *The Smart*

Set were interested in others which owed their inception to her. And he was counting upon the New York *World* to take an article he had written, inspired by her, of course. All told, he had made or stood to make seventy-eight or eighty dollars that coming month, on account of her. A fine flare of genius, to be sure, I thought. Here is certainly the result of true love, the inspiration and the fire it is supposed to induce. Just the same I could not help wondering how they were to make out on seventy-eight dollars a month.

But regardless of what I thought could or could not be done on seventy-eight dollars a month, the thing worked out after a fashion. They took over one of those bare single rooms in the heart of the Village rented to aspirants of one grade and another, but in one of its meanest streets. This they furnished with a bed, a table and a chair, also a mirror for her. Here the poet set up his exceedingly few belongings, his books and writing paper, and behind an improvised wall curtain she hung her few clothes. The first time I called there I was struck with the bareness of the floor and walls. A few old books of the cheapest fourth- and fifth-hand character, but all of them relating to matters of considerable interest, were upon the poet's table, their edges to the wall. A pile of cheap newspaper copy paper, purloined possibly from some newspaper office, showed on what he intended to scribble his great verse. No pictures, no decorations, no hangings. But, for ornament, Esther Norn herself, before whom he seemed always to gesture and genuflect as one would before an image of a saint. And why not? Would I not have done as much—and gladly?

It was Esther here and Esther there, as I soon saw. Esther had said this, and Esther had said that. Esther, the beautiful, the wonderful, the glorious, had condescended to love him, the uncouth, the unworthy, the tramp. And all this he said before me and others in her presence, bending upon her an appreciative radiant and a to me at times altogether lovely smile. This she returned with a mild and yet understanding look of affection which seemed to say and know that all he had to offer her, as he insisted, was his art, his verse, his adoration. But look you, whoever you were —he was offering her this daily and hourly. Before me and others, in a crazy, extravagant, decidedly uncouth way at times, he would seize her hands and kiss them. Or, being very much taller, he would bend over and kiss her bright red hair or temples. And then, with a queer, arch, apologetic and almost abject smile that was characteristic of him at times, a smile like the vague and wintry mirth of a lunatic, he would add: "Esther lets me do this because she loves me. She knows that I am not worthy of her—only some of the poetic thoughts I think are worthy of her, some of the thoughts she inspires in me, my thoughts of her. They are the only ones that are really worthy of her." And then he would gaze at you and at her as though he expected you to note how really striking and sincere he was, how much the poet, how much he wished that the whole world could see, as though he would give anything to see it all set forth on the first page of the morning paper or before the news reel camera of a cinema. Queer! as I used to think to myself, and yet although a bit wild,—even eerie, still beautiful in its way. As for her, at times she looked at him in silence, curiously, appraisingly, sometimes with a faint smile that might have spelled anything or nothing, or all in one—amusement, contempt, pity, kindly tolerance, affection, even a kind of motherly admiration, such admiration as a mother gives to a cooing, crowing, jumping baby. I used to wonder just what the nature of their private conversations might be. Was it possible for her to reduce him to sanity, or silence even? If she could not, for periods at least, I wondered how she endured him at all.

But this was only one phase of that life. Being an egotist, a wilding-poet, an avowed devotee of naturalism and the uncompromising enemy of all social shams and subterfuges, it was necessary for him on all possible occasions to indulge in the most direct and oftentimes disconcerting and offensive names and phrases for things for which, long since, society has troubled to discover polite euphemisms. The necessities of the body must be insisted upon in primal words, and one must say how, what, when, where. Naked to the world were all of the relations and actions ordinarily not naked. Recalling her customary reserve and silence, I gathered that (perhaps because of her curiously sniveling, deceptive, recessive father) she had come to look upon such a hearty, open return to the nomenclature of the spade as if not exactly essential, at least tonic. Mayhap, as I sometimes thought, she had become impressed with the necessity for a certain percentage of defiance of sham and convention for which this whole region seemingly stood. Also I think she may have been impressed with the long and seemingly instinctive fight he had made to rid himself of all the vestiges of the commonplace, or rather conventional, his almost insane struggle to be the free, crazy, different sort of thing that he was. And, again, perhaps she liked the publicity, or better yet the notoriety, that attended him, for it most certainly did,—even, the considerable talk as to the strangeness, the almost inexplicable nature of this union of theirs. At any rate she endured or accepted all this with that same bland, inscrutable smile, at times seemingly amused, at others indifferent, mayhap even contemptuous. At bottom only he could know or guess whether she ever heartily approved of him, and I sometimes wondered whether he even troubled to do so, so wholly self-centered he appeared to be.

If any one imagines from all this though that he was deeply or emotionally interested in any arrangement which would keep him from a nightly attendance upon the various Village dining rooms, theaters and studios in which previously he had disported himself to the amusement if not the interest of all, they are greatly mistaken. As the light to the moth so these to this erratic jack, who must run wherever he might to argue or declaim or be seen. What were home interests to this? In so far as I could gather, each moment of the day and night, but more particularly of the night, was precious from the point of view of publicity—because of the possibilities of publicity for himself that it held. If only he could be seen, heard, recalled by some one! If only he could read his verse somewhere! If only he could rise and denounce some cause or proclaim some theory or shout his approval or disapproval of something! And then, having done so, a bland, sheepish, almost appealing smile on his face, he would sink to his seat as much as to say: "Kind friends, do but think well of me. I mean so well." You have seen a dog bark savagely and then run forward wagging its tail in the hope of a little approval or petting? So he. But so human! One could not help liking him at times for the obviousness as well as the naïveté of quite all that he did. A child grown to manhood but still a child.

But to return to Esther Norn. That she was ever a party to these ebullient flitterings and posturings in any aiding or abetting sense I doubt. In fact, on these his many expeditions I heard, as well as often saw for myself, that usually she was not with him. Possessing a profound individuality which called for expression in various separate and direct individual ways, it was natural that she should not be. He must be allowed to run and play by himself. If she was with him at all she was more likely to be off in another part of the room with another group. From the first, and this I noted with interest, she was neither impressed nor dismayed by the vagaries to which he lent himself everywhere and anywhere. Neither was he sufficient of a magnet to her to claim more than a passing nod or smile from her—a gentle and affectionate smile always, to be sure. Wherever they were, together or separate, he appeared to be traveling in one intellectual direction or along one mental groove, and she another. And yet they met on the common ground of affection, I presume. In a little while their goings to and fro were looked upon as a commonplace. Both appeared to remain as before. She appeared to retain her suave and quiet individuality, he his eccentricities, his explosive and bizarre manner and dress. The thing that interested me about this marriage was that it was so different from the one that had gone before. Her first love was so correct, so well-dressed, well-mannered, well-placed, well-financed, and she had been in love with him, or so it was said. And yet she had been able to relinquish him without a pang, or at least the public show of one, and had been able to take up with this wilding, this blue-jay.

Another thing that interested and puzzled me was how she, having enjoyed a year or so of comparative affluence, could thus turn and return to the level she had endured before. For assuredly this erratic-minded poet had little to offer her other than his adoration; and I doubt if she took that without some seasoning. She was far too intelligent and sympathetic not to understand not only his best qualities but his worst, and forgive them too. And her comments on him from time to time, to me and others, proved most definitely that she did so understand him. But that is neither here nor there. One thing is certain: with him she had less, very much less, than when she was with the individual who had first interested her. And with that less she endured for a period of some three years or more.

During this time I noted that the few interesting clothes she had come by in her contact with the one man of means she had been in touch with were worn and worn until they were no longer wearable. When they were gone she took to wearing a sturdy dress of brown corduroy and a brown tam-o'-shanter with a brown wool throw of a different shade, which endured and endured until you could have told her anywhere as many as three or four short blocks away. And of course Doane was always the same as to clothing, rough unshined shoes, no hat, no overcoat as a rule, his frieze shirt always gray and sometimes open at the neck, and in cold weather beating his arms and hands together to keep them warm and yet insisting that he was not cold and that he enjoyed the chill and nip of bitter days, that they made him more active, hence healthier and more poetic. I used to laugh. When he could corner a listener he would deliver a long tirade against stoves and steam radiators and stuffy rooms and pale lymphatic people. At bottom he was right, very,— but too much of it could become a bit tiresome.

Apart from clothes and health and strength, there were the matters of food and rent, and these in so far as I could see were never properly solved during all their days together. He could not or would not do other than write poems for a living, and with her heart, and later her lungs, affected and steadily growing more troublesome, she could not work at anything which required strength. She could not, and I did not blame her. To have seen a flower like that set to an utter menial task would have been painful. Nature does not intend beauty and spirit for any such purpose, I am sure.

Hence, during all of this time and because of this binding passion, they were hard put to it to get along. How often I have met her, seemingly going somewhere on some important or urgent errand, yet if invited to breakfast or lunch, even to dinner, she would pause in her progress and accept, yet with Doane in the background somewhere but not accounted for. At such times I used to wonder what if anything he thought, whether he complained. And my humble fires—how often during that period did my doorbell ring and there would be Esther in her little tam-o'-shanter and brown corduroy and brown throw.

"Busy?" "Not at all. Come on in." And in she would come and throwing off her throw would take a pillow or two and seat herself before the hard coal open fire, studying the red radiance with the quiet, peaceful, comfort-loving affection of a cat. And unless I was very curious as to something I would return to my work, rewarded occasionally for my cordiality by a faint flicker of a smile turned in my direction. If I troubled to ask questions she would answer, all the news that she knew, but with not a trace of irritating criticism or vainglorious gossip in anything she related. Thus I heard of Doane and what he did and what she was doing, and of many others. Betimes she was helping in some Village store, betimes she was rehearsing for a play, betimes she was doing nothing because she was not feeling well. Also I heard of her father and what he was doing. Once I said: "Esther, tell me. Just what do you think of your father? We will admit that you love him as a daughter, but apart from that?" And for answer she turned to the fire, thinking. Finally she turned back. "He is just a clerk, you know," she said. "He has never had any talent for anything but that. And he's been too crazy about women, I think. He couldn't help that, of course, but he hasn't been able to manage them or his home very well. He's never been able to make any money, and now he's getting to the place where he hardly sees how to take care of himself any more. I'm sorry for Papa, but I have never been able to do very much for him."

And sometimes we discussed Doane. She knew that despite all his eccentricities I rather liked him and that I harbored no criticism of her interest in or her relations with him. "You know," she once said, "I know that you wonder about me and him. I will tell you about that. He is eccentric, a little weird at times. I know that some people think he is a little crazy. And he is a terrible egotist. He just can't help loving publicity and seeing himself as a genius and a strong man. But there is something else there, a love of beauty, and what's more, he is not as strong as he pretends to be. To me he is more like a little boy who is hungry for recognition and sympathy, who is actually crying for a little attention. Sometimes when he is talking loudest and boasting most I see just a little child with very weak little hands hanging onto his mother's skirt and crying, and then I feel intensely sorry for him. I can't help it. I know that he needs me, and I need to help him. I feel better and stronger for doing it."

"Very fine," I said, "but what about yourself? It is sufficient to you that you help him, I presume?"

For reply she nodded in the affirmative, then after a time added: "I could do something for myself if I had the strength, but I really don't know whether it would be more important." We said no more. I liked Doane well enough not to wish him any bad luck.

But just the same I noticed that as with other men so he. In spite of his gratitude to her for her goodness in deigning to notice him still he could not help but

look here and there, occasionally even straying elsewhere, the lust for the beauty of women being very
high in him. As a matter of fact, before and after he
met her, I never knew any one whom I thought more
beholden to the fair sex for their favor than he. In
Esther Norn's presence he was discreet and cool enough.
But take him when she was not present—the almost
abject craving for the attention of women—and to
their faces—a kind of slavish fawning for so much as a
look or a smile. This seemed explicable enough in the
lusty male not given to protesting too much but a little
thin and even distasteful when considered in connection with the flowery and melodramatic protesta-
tions he was accustomed to make in Esther's presence
and in that of others in regard to her.

But before I set forth examples of this I should put
down an incident which related to the two of them
and in the light of which his conduct was all the
more—well, let us say inexplicable, since it conflicted
with his mood in this case. About the time that their
union was growing to be a commonplace, say about
the end of the second year, and possibly because she
had begun to note this defection or because their
financial situation compelled it, she set forth in search
of work upon the stage and in her peregrinations one
day came upon a famous New York manager, an
American, with all the variety and color of his many
semi-romantic, semi-realistic productions and the number of stars he had made written large upon him. And

in a current, timely way he really was a notable and fairly interesting fellow—with good stage technique if no great power of thought. I knew him quite well. And it interested me to learn, as I soon did, that he was very much taken with Esther, for it was not long, as time proved, before his car, his purse, his influence were at her service had she but chosen to make use of them.

This was the way it had come about. She had drifted into his office with a letter and he, arrested by her personality, had talked very seriously with her. She had beauty, brains, and that elusive something which he said appealed to him and to the public. If she were really in earnest and would put herself at his call he would begin that day, forsooth, to provide her not only with a means of livelihood but the training which would eventually land her in a stellar rôle. For he believed in her—her stage possibilities. But in order to train her properly and to suit her time to his, or his to hers, she must be at his beck and call in so far as hours were concerned. To-day he might be in Atlantic City, to-morrow at one of the nearby beaches or at his country place in Westchester or his apartment in town. Wherever he was and he sent for her she was to come. Since she had no means he would see that a car would come to get her and return her to the stage in time (for, to begin with, he proposed to place her in a small part in one of his plays) or her home. But at his beck and call at all times she must be. And she might be called upon to stay wherever he was for days at a stretch in order that he could devote as many spare moments to her training as possible. Before ever proposing all this, however, he had asked her if she were married, and for the practical purposes of the situation she had declared that she was not. Only tentatively, though, had she accepted the opportunity, asking before accepting or rejecting a few days in which to think it over.

What followed then, as I myself witnessed, presented one of those curious tangles or cross-currents of emotions and motives such as illuminate once and for all the fol-de-rol character of all life, its inexplicable, disorderly and unfair compulsions, needs, greeds, and reasonless and insane ambitions and inhibitions. For, to begin with, here was Doane, uncertain up to this hour as to whether Esther Norn was as essential to him as she had been, (this was to be assumed from his attentions to and admirations for other women, his vehement seeking for their consideration), yet now suddenly deciding that this overture on the part of this manager presaged the certain loss of his beloved forever and concluding, if you please, that said loss would be irreparable and tragic in so far as his art was concerned, if not his very life. In so far as I could gather from rumors at the time and data that came out later, he fell to begging her not to do anything rash, almost weeping at her feet in abject despair. And then again here was Esther Norn herself, undoubtedly a sane and stable girl reasonably anxious to further herself in some way before it should prove too late, I am sure, and unquestionably dubious as to the enduring nature of this passion of Doane's for her, or of hers for him, yet pausing, so curiously vagrom is the human heart, to consider whether this suddenly aggravated need of Doane's was not after all more worthy of her consideration than this really distinguished offer, and eventually deciding that it was not within her strength or mood or charity to offend against Doane.

Yet, as I later learned, and from herself, no less, the erratic moods of this vagrom poet at this very time were causing her to pause and debate whether he could remain faithful to her or she to him. And he did not remain faithful to her, nor she to him. But I am getting ahead of my story.

The details are as follows: Doane, on first hearing of this offer, (without being told all of the conditions which accompanied it, I believe), rushed forth to all and sundry to tell of the great good fortune that had thus suddenly come to his wife and that now and henceforth they were really to be people of some importance. And all this in the face of rotund and wholesale denunciation by him in the past of all and sundry connected with the conventional stage as creatures of so low an artistic level as to be below the notice of any one. None the less Esther was now a genius and at last to be encouraged as was her due. Their fortune was to be made and at once. She was to have a small part at once in one of the great Hokum's plays. And he, Doane, I mean— But harken! Wait! Only see! He was to remain with her, as her this, her that— guide, playwright, what not. She was to get fifty or seventy-five dollars a week now, but only while she was being prepared for a real stellar rôle. Later and soon of course she would be famous and well-to-do. And—and— In fact, as I came to think from listening to him, he already saw himself in some august position beside her say, as her manager or impresario, the head and front of her artistic progress, leading her by the hand as it were and at the same time reciting his own poems to admiring throngs who were to be come at through her. Everybody had to hear the news; I doubt if there was one person in that small artistic realm who did not know of it before nightfall.

But soon a pall, a dark veil of mist, overcasting this bright scene. For, as I gathered afterward, Esther had by then made clear the terms on which this success or opportunity was to be based. There was to be a compromise. She was not likely to see as much of him as she had, for a time anyhow. Indeed, it was not unlikely that in a very little while certain advances would be made by the great Hokum which would tend to eliminate him, Doane, as her husband—unless here and now she chose to put aside and once and for all this brilliant offer. Did Doane wish that? Would he give her up or would he not? Did he think it worth

while for her to give him up? Could he do without
her?

As I gathered from others as close to them as I
was, at the time this struck him as an outrageous and
terrible proposition, cruel, worthy only of one of those
dogs of wealth and fame and position who sit at the
top in life and do ill to the helpless and so downtrodden. Ho! only think! A rich, powerful man like
that, a Dives, no less, sitting daily and hourly at his
loaded table, gorged to the craw with the fat and luxuries of life, yet into the bargain now attempting to
approach and by chicane or treachery take from him,
a great if starving world-poet, his one ewe lamb. And
Esther, his own Esther no less, venturing to even consider such a thing! Jehovah! Justice! This scoundrel,
this beast, this reveler, this satyr! (Will some one only
unloosen my collar from my choking throat?) With
all things at his command, as it were, the world at
his feet, yet daring to propose to a poor struggling
girl like Esther, this lovely, gentle thing, such a dreadful, such a shameful compromise as this! Oh, woe, woe,
woe! And he had been and was so fond of Esther.
Oh, woe, woe, woe! To better herself she was expected
to yield herself, her priceless self, to such a scoundrel!
And for what? In order to win the privilege of ex-
ercising that innate artistry which was hers! Horrible
—a shameful infraction of all the natural laws of opportunity! Think of a dog like that attaining to the
position in the theatrical world where he could thus

dictate the terms of opportunity to a young and beautiful girl of talent! And think of there being poor girls of genius who might be and no doubt were at times compelled to submit to such outrageous use! A man such as that should undoubtedly be drummed out of the stage world. He should be exposed for what he was: a scoundrel, a waster of young flesh, a Gorgon, an ogre. Things were certainly come to a pretty pass in this world when such things could be.

At the same time, as I noted for myself, there was a covert sort of pride in him, which sprang from the fact that so powerful and prosperous and important a man (a bounder and an artistic nobody when it came to the higher arts—such as poetry, for instance) should stoop to interest himself in such a girl as Esther.

However, as it turned out, his tears and prayers were effective. Esther quietly gave over the prospect. And Doane, seeing that he personally was now responsible for this sacrifice and that local opinion as such might now be divided as to the wisdom of her conduct and his share in it, was for taking counsel of all and sundry as to whether, after all, he had done the right thing. Was he to blame for thinking and feeling as he did? Was Esther, regardless of his own moods and fatal pangs wrong in listening to him or taking his advice? He even came to me with this proposition and I went over it with him—finally quite flatly stating that if Esther really believed that the opportunity was a great one and that she might succeed she should have taken it. And with this he went away saying that I was right and that no doubt he was wrong. None the less they began to slip back into their old ways and the incident was soon forgotten. They remained as poor as ever, of course, and Doane after a time—a few months, say six—began to devote himself to other attractive women, in his tentative, seeking, poetic way.

But now followed phases which interested me as much if not more than those that had gone before. During the very hard winter that followed (the third of the great war) they lived more poorly than ever. As I have said, Doane never had a dollar over and above rent and gas-bills unless he borrowed it. And Esther Norn wore that same corduroy suit but with no warm coat and no suitable shoes and no satisfactory heat in their chamber. Owing to her developing heart and lung trouble she was not strong, and it was during this winter that she took a severe cold which turned into a serious case of pneumonia and eventually into consumption. From this last, I may add, she never really recovered. Yet it was during this very winter (and as much during the severest period of her illness as at any other time) that Doane was about as much as ever, in the restaurants, the little theaters, the studios, and where not else, reciting, denouncing, explaining his plans, putting himself forward as the apostle and the apotheosis of the simple, the abstemious, the sincere, the honest, the kind, the frank, the true, the good even. It was wonderful. And his wife at this very time lying at home, wanting for what certainly may be described as the necessaries of life— suitable heat and food, pleasant surroundings, satisfactory clothing, competent medical service. He was no more capable of doing for her, apparently, than was a child. As I saw it, his was a dizzy egotistic form of self-esteem which would not permit him to undertake anything manual or clerical. Worse, he had not yet found himself from a literary and mental point of view and either could not or would not write anything save poetry, and that, in the main, poetry which was not acceptable to the magazines. Throughout the winter I think there were times when they were both underfed and not always warm. A girl that I knew, noting that Esther Norn wore the same dress in season and out, finally bought the material for a dress and made it for her. She wore this for a time but later laid it aside on the ground that it did not look as well on her as the one she had before. More than once this erratic poet borrowed wherever he could, a dollar here, two dollars there, as much as ten from me once and another time perhaps the same amount. I neither, I may say here, desired or expected a return. It was all a part of village life. But, just the same, wherever and whenever we met thereafter he was for explaining why it was that he had not paid me, until at last I asserted that unless he ceased I would eventually exact payment, whereupon the matter was closed. But that was one of his ways of dramatizing his seemingly pinched life. It was colorful to worry about unpaid bills.

That winter it was, though, that Esther Norn grew very weak because of the pneumonia which could never be dislodged, at least not under the circumstances which governed in her case. Their room was so cold that they were forced to move, and to add to this her father, a by now most anæmic and insufficient person, came to live with them in the two small rooms and bath into which from the other they now moved. Then later and from Doane himself I began to hear tales relative to this new life. Her "old man," as he characterized him, was a this and a that, a loafer, a drunkard, and a what not. He would not work. He had no brains. He had never done anything for his daughter and could not now. "Sure, he pays four dollars a week rent," he once said to me, "but then he borrows nearly all of it back before the week's out, and Esther, like a damned fool, gives it to him. He never pays it to me," he added, with a note of pained regret. On another occasion he stated that he suspected her of lending small sums to her father over and above this. Whose money it was that she loaned he did not say.

But this also was a mere nothing as contrasted with some deeper things which by now had begun to manifest themselves in connection with these two. For about such a noisy, aggressive temperament as was Doane's there will always gather some who are interested, if by nothing more than a spectacle of activity and un-rest. The clown, the performer upon a trapeze, one who keeps eight or ten brightly colored balls spin-ning, will most certainly cause many to pause and note. It is better than nothing. At any rate there were a number, men and women, boys and girls, who were interested by Doane. He amused them, and he himself was always hopelessly fascinated by the spec-tacle of youth and charm in the other sex. It was not, I think, that he was vastly lascivious. I cannot even imagine that; but rather that he was fascinated by the thought of love and that he was interesting to women and women were interested in him on that score as well as on the other that he was a poet and a great man, or a prospective great man. And so it was in the cards or the stars that, buzzing around him as he was, there should be one or more who would take his fancy, espe-cially since he was much alone these days.

There was, for instance, one girl, the daughter of a woman doctor whom I knew, a young, pretty, sensual thing, almost as erratic and harum-scarum as Doane himself, who swam into his net. From the girl's mother I learned that she was having a hard time in trying to prevent an affair here. He was fascinated and so was the girl. He was aggressive and the girl not un-willing. To end it all the mother threatened to appeal to his sick wife, which after a time caused him to desist. But he resented this interference on the part of the mother as an infraction of his own and her daughter's rights.

Then there was a tall, graceful, romantic thing who wrote some poetry. She wore changeful and emotional clothes and held changeful and emotional views in regard to freedom, self-development, the need of finding stimulating and enlightening experiences and the like. Either she pretended or enjoyed an affection for Doane which lasted long after Esther was better. It was generally admitted that there was an affectional relationship here, but whether only of the mind or not I cannot say. Of one thing I am sure: It was not of the mind alone toward the last, when Esther Norn was no more. The most interesting of all these divagations on his part which came to my ears was one which appeared to follow hard upon a trip to the country made possible for Esther during her illness by a well-to-do radical, who, however, did not choose to invite Doane. The trip lasted a month or six weeks, during which time Doane remained in the city.

It was during this absence of Esther's though that Doane was busy with another affair, this time devoting himself to a varietistic Venus whose mania for affairs, long before he had arrived on the scene, had attracted much amused attention in this part of the world. Charming she was and intellectual, but the equal of Esther Norn? Never. But that is neither here nor there. What was interesting to me was that after his great excitement about the manager and hard upon his wife's illness he could follow this hard and laughing and more or less indifferent lady in true troubadour fashion, *on foot,* to some mountains in northern New York, whither she had gone for the summer. "Oh, yes. Leif Doane! What a dear, foolish, crazy boy he is, anyhow. You know he followed me to Granite Lodge on foot last June, the dear boy. He didn't have carfare, so he walked. But I didn't know that then; if I had I'd have given it to him. But these poets! Sometimes, I do declare, romance can become a little cloying, don't you think? One hardly knows what to do with a cloud-riding poet such as that at times."

Then descriptions, with exact dates.

This was not the only phase of an interesting and to me kaleidoscopic and somewhat bizarre romance. Although after her illness, which lasted for months, Esther Norn was not as strong as she had been, still she was once more up and about. To me she was now more beautiful than she had been. There was something spiritual and mediæval about her very pale face, her red hair, her still blue eyes and her greatly reduced figure and greatly reduced strength. Together they suggested fragility, the delicacy of a flower. The unnatural bloom of her cheeks now, due to the disease that had attacked her and that never after was successfully repulsed, added to her charm. I used to pause when I saw her, arrested by the glow which had already been noted by many.

Naturally I wondered what she thought of her relationship to Doane by now. Did she know? Was she troubled? Or was she unconscious of his mental vagaries? After a time I gathered that she did know. Also that before ever she gave herself to him she had realized fully that he was a weak and variable creature whose attentions could never be wholly confined to herself. For once she said in my presence: "Leif? Oh, yes. I can guess. It's very hard for him to resist pretty women. He has to have attention. He needs it so much." It was during this time that they were living in the small bare suite in Eleventh Street. Sometimes her father was about, sometimes not. Ditto Doane. As before, her poet-husband or playmate was busy about various things, reciting his latest compositions in the public restaurants that went in for that sort of thing, hanging about the library and dancing floor of the Liberal Club and there emphasizing his greatness to all and sundry or arguing vociferously for strength, sincerity, a Spartan contempt for luxury; also hanging about the Brevoort, the Lafayette and other expensive places where the cognoscenti gathered, and in these spending in a grand manner whatever small sums of cash he could come by; and then borrowing, visiting the various editors with his poems, or working betimes at some task or other in connection with one of the minor theaters of the district. The more I thought of him and Esther Norn the less I could understand how to herself she justified her refusal of the great manager.

But then on the heels of this came one of the most

curious developments of all. To really understand you would have to know the world of parlor radicalism, anarchism, socialism, communism and progress as it relates to self-development or better yet self-advancement generally. It is easy to rattle off words of dim or pseudo import. But to have known, as have I, the many men of means and university degrees who by reason of an inheritance or the gift of making a comfortable living in a leisurely or crafty way, such as the law or trade, or what you will, are thereby enabled to set up as authorities in the arts, economics, politics and reform and to pose as patrons or saviors of the masses, the downtrodden, etc., is to have known the very substance of futility or craft, or both. It has been an interested privilege in my case to have known and observed from time to time one and another of these, but among them none more closely than J. J.

We will admit, firstly, that he was a man of broad understanding, sensitivity, and some learning, yet intellectually convinced of the futility of everything—life, death, energy, faith, disillusion, men—whatever you will. A cold light, as it were. At times he appeared to wonder why he or any one else chose to exist. On the other hand, he appeared to be sufficiently sound and vigorous and voracious materially or physically, as to enjoy himself hugely, to eat, drink and make merry with the best. To do him justice, though, in the course of a number of years, he had written a series of social studies which were of considerable interest, even if they got nowhere nor threw any definite constructive light on anything. Somewhat labored, they were still interesting as pictures. Finding in frequent periods of intoxication relief from a mental ennui that followed upon contemplating things as they are, he had become a little marked by that. Also temperamentally a gourmand, he was stout, but still attractive. At the time Esther Norn came to know him he was still industriously searching out new and peculiar surroundings under which to live and enjoy himself. Also, although married and the father of four children, he was not above varietistic experiences and turned now to one and now to another of the opposite sex, seeking always, I am sure, freedom from ennui. New affectional contacts were common with him, the everillusioning fevers of passion and romance.

With all this I must add, curious as it may seem, that he was a little close where money was concerned. Several disastrous investments and the knowledge that he had no plan for making additional cash out of the money he had inherited, had made him almost unduly cautious. But in spite of this and due to the fact that contact with the other sex seemed to set up an enlivening flame in him, he interested women who off-hand, one might have said, would not have wasted a look upon him. Although his residence and his family were in the country—a most rural estate, by the way—he was frequently to be found about the restaurants and resorts of the radical section of the city. Indeed, he was known to and not on bad terms with scores of those who were interested in the arts and letters. And anent the various economic and social agitations of the day it was most interesting to listen to him. He could talk, and talk convincingly. In short, he was looked upon, by radicals or at least the pseudo-radicals of the world about which I am writing, as very interesting and very well-to-do, but cautious and dilettante, a parlor or library radical.

I have drawn him thus at length because of the marked part he played in the closing aspects of Esther Norn's life. Up to this time he had not met her, but he had known of if he did not actually know her husband. In regard to Doane he once observed to me that he was a person in whom he could not possibly be interested. He was an ego-maniac, too futile, one who possessed no genuine flair for the arts. But a part of this lack of appreciation might have sprung from the fact that at that time Doane was young and he was already forty-five or fifty and gray. And Doane was fantastic and physically active, whereas by now J. was inclined to be lethargic and mentally sober.

Let that be as it will. After the crisis in connection with the celebrated manager through which Doane and his wife had come, and after Doane's several tentative approaches and retreats here and there, J. J. appeared as the friend and occasional companion of Esther Norn. And then, after a few months, there floated here and there reports of an intense and profoundly emotional affair which these twain were undergoing. At first I could scarcely believe this. The difference in their ages, their temperaments—or at least as I judged their temperaments at the moment. Later thinking of Doane, and then her first love and her father I was not so sure. For a time anyhow, and if you please, they disappeared, but only to reappear later in the world with which both were so familiar. But in so far as I could learn there was no change in the domestic or other arrangements which still existed between Doane and Esther and her father. None. All lived in the same place as before, only now they were rarely seen together. Interestingly enough, J. J., in addition to his place in the country, had now taken a floor in one of the more pleasing parts of the Village and from time to time he and Esther Norn were to be seen together.

But to me, psychologically and practically, the thing had so many quirks and twists that I could not let it alone. To begin with, there was the individual with whom she had been in love before ever she had known Doane, a presentable and interesting man, self-contained, fairly liberal, and obviously respectable and kindly. Then there was Doane, bounding and alive, if unreliable and helpless. Then there was the manager, really the most able and artistic of all and the one who could have done most for her, whom she had rejected for Doane. And now this interesting but rather unstable and changeable J. J.

And by him most of all in this particular instance

was I impressed. For, to sum up J. J., one would have
said that at his time of life and with his changeful,
restless and kaleidoscopic past, to say nothing of his
present family ties and social inhibitions, he had nothing to offer any young and attractive woman. Admitting brains, position and means, still, by reason
of a strain of *caste* that ran through all his thoughts
and actions, almost any one could have detected that
he would do little more than condescend to any relationship which did not spell some social advantage to
himself. In short, such a point of view was little more
than second nature with him. By birth, training and
that freedom which sprang from means liberally provided by his parents had he come to feel that he belonged to a world above and apart from the common
herd. And that common herd included all who lacked
means and position, even such a girl as Esther, say.
At the same time, as I have tried to indicate, a certain
liberality of mind or temperament had caused him to
seek out and interest himself in such especial figures
of the mass as chanced to show that they had thoughts
and aspirations apart from the level on which they
had been born. Finally there is this to be said for
him: he did not look entirely like one whom self-satiation had caused to become cruel or indifferent to the
moods or needs of others. He still had an easy, genial,
play-dog air which was most deceptive. To not a few it
concealed the fact that he was as self-centered and
as indifferent spiritually as it is humanly possible to be.

And in proof of this I was quick to note that on the material side Esther was not profiting by this contact. Rather her bleak social and material life seemed to go on as before. She lived, ate, dressed about as before.

Meeting her on the street one day during the height of this affair, I fell in with her and we walked a little way together. She was silent for a time but a hundred paces farther on she said: "You can't help thinking of me and J. J., can you?" "No, I can't," I replied. "Well, just to make it a little clearer to you, I count it a wonderful experience, one of the most wonderful of my life and most helpful to me. I felt you might not understand. But this is true." "I am prepared to believe it," I replied. "I presume like Doane he needs you as much as you need him." "I don't know as to that. I only know that I need him. I need the mental lift he gives me." I have often thought of that since. No doubt it was true.

But later J. J., learning of this encounter, I presume, came to my door, bearing a bundle of short essays or prose poems which to my surprise he proceeded to unfold, whereupon I discovered that they related to Esther Norn and himself, his love for her and hers for him. "I wish you would read these, or let me read them to you," he said. "You will understand them. And Esther wanted me to show them to you. I've been writing them from time to time during the last six weeks." I took them and read, one, ten, a score, then paused, for I saw the drift of all of them. They were semi-philo-

sophic, semi-erotic and in certain ways highly romantic
discourses on love and beauty and the deeper or esoteric
meaning of passion and character, yet relating specifi-
cally to at the same time that they attempted to eluci-
date the various shades or moods of this great emotional
tie which had sprung up between Esther and himself,
their respective spiritual or poetic attitudes toward
beauty and the mental or psychic call that had drawn
them together. According to him Esther was marvelous
—a "world soul"—a true flower of the spirit and these
effusions of his the finest, the most mature and the
most beautiful of all his mental flights so far. (The
wonder of emotion, I thought; of passion; of sex, the
great, the dominating force!) And actually they were
very good, some of them, splendid. Quite obviously
they were inspired by a chemic something which had
refreshed and revivified J. J.'s imagination and hers,
for the time being anyhow. In a different way from his
ordinary or more sober and philosophic approach to
life, as I saw it then, he was attempting to do what
Doane had sought to do before him—express the passion and delight with which Esther Norn had inspired him. Only Doane's way was to dance about and
kiss her hands and cry: "Esther lets me do this because
she loves me. She knows that I am not worthy of her—
only some of the poetic thoughts I think are worthy of
her." Whereas J. J.'s way was to compose semi-sober
and philosophic papers or essays, each aglow with a
somber, fading resigned tenderness that was shot

through with an aching fear of conclusion. I felt sorry for him, for I felt that so great an emotion at this time must be to him, if not Esther, an enormous and perhaps destructive psychic strain. He could not burn so fiercely and live.

Our Anglo-Saxon world is I think much too cold toward and even intolerant of any expression of the love or creative passion after the years of eighteen to thirty. Apparently it sees but dimly, if at all, that years do not destroy the passions of the heart or brain, or if it does it prefers to deny and repress. If life is so, it should not be and hence as I chance to know J. J. was the subject of much chilly speculation and comment just at this time. Esther too for interesting herself in him. None the less J. J.'s years had left him with real ability. Mentally Doane could not hope to cope with him. For that reason and to me at any rate, it was interesting to note all this and for the life of me I could not help thinking what a curious and different sort of girl this must be who could if not at once at least so violently interest two such very different men and could be interested by them. Most certainly here must be some spiritual or poetic values over and above the animal. And she had discovered them to Doane and J. J., possibly to others who had interested her; and all of them were more respectable in my eyes for having been able to interest her.

But this again was something that was destined to fade into thin air, as does all romance, apparently, whether violently interrupted or unimpeded or not. In this last case, I presume, this process was all the more quickly aided by the practical and conventional considerations which affected J. J. His was a nature which was certain to weary of anything. Once they were over, such affairs as this, however violent or emotional their nature at the time, were listed as curious or valuable mental or emotional reactions, according to the measure or character of the artistic or intellectual stimulus he had received at the time. Such-and-such an affair here, there or elsewhere had provided him with such-and-such conclusions or deductions. I do not believe that Esther Norn was either so cool or so precise in her intellectual summation of her life and affairs.

However that may be, the lapse of a year suddenly brought a crisis in the affairs of J. J. which served to darken or rather change this moving and poetic situation for him. His oldest boy, a loving, intelligent and yet romantic youth on whom he doted and whom he had placed in a western technical school, was suddenly blotted out by some contagious disease, and that before either of his parents could reach him, and that when this affair with Esther Norn was still at high tide. This sudden blow dealt to him by life seemed to have a most disturbing effect upon him, more than I would have anticipated. As it was a profound and dark despair enveloped upon him, so dark and so crushing as to cause him to pause and in a vain and, as I saw it, decidedly weak emotional state to seek to revalue all his values. Was he right in leading the life that he had led? Was individualism as opposed to socialism in the affectional sense all wrong? His philosophic and practical deductions in regard to all he had seen here on earth, what about them? One night at about ten o'clock in my old Tenth Street Studio I was suddenly confronted by a morbid and weeping man, old and desolate-looking and slightly the worse, I am sorry to report, for having taken refuge in drink. And now brokenly telling me of this his perhaps first great, psychic shock. His boy! His boy! Bereft! Bereft! Shaken to the very roots of his being, apparently, he was moved to question (after the fashion of the religious "sinner" of old) the spiritual or ethical relationship of all his past deeds to himself, his children, his wife, life, or the controlling forces of the universe. Perhaps, as he now said to me, and with wet eyes, there was something more than accident to the theory of conduct and relationship or duty now holden by so many in the economic and social stresses of life. Perhaps, if not a God, at least something, some chemic or psychic balance, concealed in all things and making for responsibility and order, or the necessity for them. Might it not punish evasion with a Karma-like retribution, and here and now rather than later. In other and simple words, "Vengeance is mine, saith the Lord; I will repay."

Truly we can admit that from every deed proceeds the impulse or force therof. Yet to where exactly? And the sum and substance of many despicable actions may possibly tend to inferences as to despicability in oneself and others wherever intelligence reigns. I am free to admit as much, and was at that time. But I was not quite willing to admit that primarily man, the lorn single individual rooted so deeply and inextricably as he is in the forces that underlie and bring him into being and motivate him so mechanistically, could be so completely responsible for all that he does, feels, is driven to feel. Why not life? God? Electrons? Protons? Electricity itself. Why not? Mechanism plus behaviorism, as you see, had seized upon me. Yet seeing so much and saying so much, I could not quite respect the cringing backfire of such a mood as this. While I did not blame him entirely I could and most certainly did hold in contempt the concatenation of forces and moods and chemic emanations or arrangements which could bring about such a blubbering recession from moods which but an hour or a week before were so diametrically opposed to all this. Much as I really loved his boy and sorry as I felt for him and his wife, I could not help saying as much. And I could not help but contrast his deep sensitiveness to this his personal loss with his ordinary urbane and genial dismissal of all the woes of others as economic and chemic movements which at bottom could not really be the deep concern of any one. We did not quarrel exactly but from me he got not so much emotional support as he probably expected and soon left.

But the blight which this cast upon his relations with Esther Norn from now on was of interest. A curious and almost impalpable change, this. For a month or more after his boy's death he was to be found only about his country place, to which the body was brought. And later, once he did appear, he was of a different and soberer mood than of yore. He even seemed to have aged greatly. Unquestionably a marked tendency toward a varietistic if not orgiastic form of living had been replaced by a desire to do differently, for the time being anyhow. In the course of time it was to be observed that he spent less of his time with the one who had so recently proved so profound and shaking an experience, and more and more with the family he had hitherto placed secondary to his other adventures. That he entertained and retained a sincere and kindly affection for Esther, I know. Throughout a later period, which was now fast approaching, he was of some financial if no great affectional service to the one who had lately interested him so intensely.

But following this psychic smash and with his going Esther Norn appeared to find her individuality once more and was again to be seen about the old haunts that had known her. And about six months after the death of J. J.'s son she was once more playing a very small rôle in one of the local theaters but not with any too much strength, for it was understood that not only was she afflicted with consumption which could not be made to yield, but that her none too well constructed heart was giving her more trouble. Finally, at the end of a very warm and depressing summer, she was ill again, this time irrecoverably, with a combination of rapid lung deterioration and a disturbingly weak heart.

This news spread. For Doane, ever impecunious and in need, was not backward in making plain the hard physical lines upon which Esther had fallen. She was very ill. It was doubtful if she could ever recover. And her "old man" was of no use to her; he did not even pay his own board. And as for himself, he had only sold two poems to so-and-so for five dollars each in a month, and but one to so-and-so for three. And upon these he would not be able to realize for some time to come. So in the meantime— Need I suggest what, in the meantime? Decidedly though there was something moving if irritatingly pitiable about it all. For one could not help but think of Esther Norn, with her delicate white face, her blue eyes, her bronze hair and her dreamy, speculative conception of life and things, lying in a shabby room without the comforts of an ordinary clerk or laborer.

And just why J. J. did not come to her rescue during this period puzzled me not a little. For and although I had always thought, and felt that having been born to wealth and position in the first instance, and being of a peculiarly self-centered and coldly speculative turn of mind in the next, it was not possible for J. J. to see a third or fourth person in any but a remote and somewhat mathematical or speculative light, still there were those poems addressed to Esther and his enormous concern for his own boy. None the less it was only when the state in which Esther now found herself had become one for general comment that J. J. came forward, along with some others, with a plan for the amelioration of her condition. It was suggested by one and another that she be sent to a sanitarium for consumptives, out of the noise and dust of New York, where she might have a fighting chance. And here eventually she was sent, at his expense, I believe, but not before others not as closely related to her had made it possible for her to be transferred to more commodious quarters nearer Fifth Avenue.

It was at this last place that I really last saw Esther. And even here were Doane and her father living with and presumably taking care of her. I wish I might believe as much. Yet at this time J. J. was confining himself almost exclusively to his estate on the Hudson. And as for Doane he was out and around at the various restaurants, parties, studios, this, that, with which the village was, and I assume remains, dotted—rarely, if ever at home. But composing poems, plays, speeches and what not else. And conducting as I recall a most unprofitable one-man theater. But just the same each time that I visited Esther she was cheerful and smiling and this in the face of the inevitable disaster that was stalking her. Positively she seemed to me to be of that same high spirit that is presumed to characterize the healthy and the successful everywhere. She breathed

neither indifference nor resignation nor despair nor yet
the least trace of discontent or dissatisfaction, but a
kind of smiling superiority and ease which spoke more
of well-being and position and comfort than anything
else. In all my experiences I had never contacted anything more serene.

And yet she did not think she was going to get well.
Her thought was that she was not, or that it did not
make any difference. Waving aside the flowers or the
fruit that I troubled to bring, she would begin a discussion of something—a book, a play, some æsthetic
Village movement, or the actions or point of view of
some individual in the world. Hers was a naturally
intuitive and forceful mind that understood without
effort. Hers was a neo-esoteric, or as the spiritualists
have it, an "old soul."

But during this time, also, I occasionally met J. J.,
but more in the Village restaurants and thought-resorts
than in this apartment. Also as I have said, Doane. And
throughout all this the attitude of Doane toward J. J.
and of J. J. toward Doane was characteristic of each.
Doane, as I was half amused to see, feigned not to
know of the relationship that had existed between J. J.
and Esther and yet spoke of both, of Esther with the
consideration due one to whom he was genuinely obli-
gated, of J. J. in or with the mood of one who admits
that a man may be of some force or worth intellectually
but beyond one's liking just the same. On the other
hand, J. J. never did bring himself, and could never

have been brought for that matter, to manifest any interest in or even to mention Doane. The poet was not of his world. At worst or best he was too erratic, too childish, too lacking in politeness and intellectual savoir-faire. In J. J.'s eyes Doane was an unimportant reformer or agitator, but in a weak sense,—not one of those threatening labor strugglers in whom he was always genuinely interested. And to Doane J. J. was a snob.

The end of it all came, as I may say with Esther's eventual transfer to a sanitarium among the pines of northern New York, where for six months she lingered and then died. I never saw her there but those who did continued the picture of one who appeared to live in a dream, ignoring the material considerations of life and thinking on beauty. She liked to read poetry and began to sketch, a branch of the æsthetics in which she had never dabbled before. The last thing she did on that day she died, or so I heard, was to write over and over the name of the erratic poet she had married and to sketch his head with certain flourishes and modifications which made it less erratic and more appealing. None the less, as I also heard, he visited her but once— he who in the heyday of another affair could troubadour-wise follow his lady love on foot all the way to the Berkshires, there to strum his adulations in her ears—if ever he did strum. His excuse—and possibly this was a respectable one—that he lacked the means wherewith to exist there. But then J. J. appeared but once. After her death, however, and after he had caused her body to be returned to New York for burial, he did send flowers and did defray all expenses. Being involved with some affairs in the West at the time, so it was said, he could not come.

As for Doane. On hearing that her last thoughts were of him he was much wrought up, so I heard, shaken with a fusion of intellectual and emotional sorrow "plus satisfaction" as some one troubled to say of him at the time—sorrow over the fact that so bright a thing as his and Esther's relationship had to fade, satisfaction that after all and notwithstanding she had still held him within the circle of her interests and sympathies. Years later, when he was living very much alone and not as much regarded by many as in other days he is said to have said to some one: "Esther was the only real inspiration I ever had—the finest thing in my life."

That I am prepared to believe.

BRIDGET MULLANPHY

Bridget Mullanphy

I THINK of her always as an integral part of one of those
blowsy, ash-can-decorated thoroughfares of New York's
lower West Side, gray granite blocks paving it,
dirt and garbage lying disgustingly uncollected, a dead
cat or dog, maybe; dirty children; dirty, dark hallways giving into the respective walls at regular intervals; a ruck of trucks and carts clattering to and fro;
but at the end the bright North River, a metal stream,
flowing at the base of the Palisades, which rise like a
gray wall above it, and above that a gray or blue sky,
ribbon-wide.

On the low step gracing the sidewalk entrance of one
of these squalid tenements, Mrs. Mullanphy, gray-
haired, burly, squarish rather than rotund, a slight in-
dentation at the middle of her sleeveless "wrapper"
indicating a former waist-line, almost always tied
around with a dirty, faded gingham apron. She has
been sweeping and is now resting upon the handle of
her broom. A slattern of a girl in a green blouse and
brown skirt, holding a baby on one arm, is talking to
her. I am about to address her, Jimmie, my man of
all work, having deserted me these several weeks, when
the following scene takes place:

Mrs. Mullanphy (*looking along the hall toward an invisible stair—invisible because of shadow—and then up at a second- or third-story window*): The likes of them! The likes of them! It's them that is the clean ones, is it, with a peck of dirt under the bed and the same blanket from one year's end to the other! 'Tis never they have a blanket on the line. (*A head appears at one of the upper windows, second story left. It is a big head, broad-faced between parted wings of dark red hair. Its owner wears a triangle of red-and-brown-squared shawl—a small shawl in no way protecting an immense bosom held in by a nightgown or "wrapper".*)

Red Head: And who is it that talks of dirt, with ashes under the stove—pans of them—and fish heads on the floor! And the health department wonderin' at the sickness in the block! (*The head disappears.*)

Mrs. Mullanphy (*looking up defiantly and shouting*): The health department, is it? The health department? And with yer own child after dyin' from dirt and little else. 'Tis diphtheria that comes from dirt, and nothin' else. And yer old man out of a job three months out of four. And yer son that drinks till 'tis himself that can't find his way through the hall and up the stairs at night but must be fallin' against the doors of other folks when they're tryin' to sleep. (*To the girl who is holding the baby*): 'Tis a bit warm, ain't it? (*Then giving a square rag of a carpet an extra flick with her broom.*)

THE GIRL WITH THE BABY: Yes, it is. Terry! Terry! Come away from that dead cat!

RED HEAD (*reappearing at the window above*): 'Tis me son, is it? And work, is it? And your old man out of work these three months now, and scabbin' in the place of better men when he does. And where is the cup of sugar borried of me these six months and not returned yet? And before that, me salt and me starch? (*The head disappears.*)

MRS. MULLANPHY: Out of work, is it? And you with yer darter on the streets of the city this day! And with men runnin' to where ye lived before till it was the vice society that was called in and yerselves put out by the police! And no rent, and yer furniture put out! Where is the can of coffee I loaned ye six weeks this Monday? Salt, is it? And yer darter out to get money from men and yer drunken son fallin' through the halls!

.   .   .   .

So there you are! I would not, I assure you, present this, nor much that is to follow, save for the strange irritability of it all; the vague, blundering, I might even say fantastic, and reasonless pother and ado that *is* life, here as well as elsewhere. And what the meaning or purpose of the creative force when it could descend to such fol-de-rol and nonsense as this, I used to ask myself on observing and listening to such a scene.

But let us return to that same doorstep a few months later. Now it is a cold, gray, almost dark November afternoon. I am again on my way to engage Mrs. Mullanphy to do some cleaning for me. I encounter little Delia Mullanphy, aged four, (although the eldest daughter of this household is in her thirties), playing house with a little boy in the dust and dirt of the sidewalk under an arc light blazing thus early on this dusky afternoon.

"And now ye're to come home at six, see?" the child is saying as she rises and pushes her little boy companion away to give him a good start on his homecoming. And he, once strategically placed as a homecomer, comes swaggering and staggering, but listen.

"Ain't dinner ready yet, hey? You ——! It's six o'clock and there ain't nothin' on the table, eh! I'll give you a punch in the jaw, you!" And with this making a vigorous, if childish, lunge. But at this strenuous point in the game I choose to interrupt with an inquiry. It is all so realistic that I fear he will strike her, wondering at the same time how two such infants come by such knowledge as this.

The second floor front right as you go up is occupied by Mrs. Mullanphy, her husband, thirty-year-old daughter and four-year-old daughter. Mullanphy père, as I understand from Mrs. Mullanphy's irrepressible patter, works very occasionally as a teamster. He works, that is, when the spirit moves him. Cornelia, the elder daughter, as I also occasionally hear from my talkative cleaning woman, works out at times;

at other times she sews at home. Mrs. Mullanphy, herself, scrubs, washes, anywhere and everywhere, as the spirit or necessity moves her. For Mullanphy, as I also well know by now, is exceedingly unreliable—a temperamental and in the main befogged Irishman who seems in part to be afraid of and in another part not to consider or be moved by his wife in any way. In truth, I cannot exactly explain how this is—a sort of marital enigma which I have never been able to solve for myself. As I ascend the stairs, however, I hear a voice, unmistakably that of my cleaning-lady, and I stop to listen to the following:

"And who is it that talks of family? Is it the Finnertys? God knows what they sprang from! Family, is it? With a son in the protectory! 'Tis me fond boast that a Mullanphy is as good as anyone, and better. They can be looked up for what they are these hundreds of years back."

(Upon my word, I thought! Such noble lineage! This is a cleaning-woman worth having.) But then came the reply, hurled down from an upper window and treasured by me to this day:

"'Tis yer proud boast, is it? And your nieces carryin' things to ye that don't belong to them! 'Tis the police that should be told of it! And yerself pretendin' to be the mother of a child not yer own! Ye old harridan! And 'tis well we can guess whose it is! And who's the father of yer darter's child? And where is he? And why isn't she with him this day, and the

child, too? A widow, is it? A foine widow! And her
and yerself leavin' Barry Street and no father there!
Widow! And she the young lady yet, still lookin' for
a man! Foine family, is it? Heaven preserve the rest
of us from such foineness!" The voice died heavily
away.

But enough of the long rigmarole of charges and re-
joinders that invariably flew about these tenement
rooms and halls, principally, as I was always pained
to note, between Mrs. Mullanphy and her neighbors
whenever I was in that region. How flesh and blood
could continuously endure them is beyond me. My own
interest might honestly be said to have been literary.
I was so thoroughly fascinated by this outspoken Irish
realism which nowhere else apparently could I find
in such undiluted and plentiful quantities that I liked
to come here. Otherwise not. For as I had already observed of other nations and races, they were much more
secretive. But the Irish never. On the contrary, in such
a world as this, it did seem as though all of the customary reserves and punctilio of better neighborhoods
or ordinary social life anywhere no longer held. Either
they had never existed for those who dwelt in this en-
vironment or they had broken down. And in addition,
whatever the reason—poverty and lack of training in
the amenities being the principal ingredients, I am sure
—a state of troublesome and devastating espionage
and criticism held. No one could do anything that
was not more or less the subject of observation

and comment. At the slightest indication of exclusiveness, public opprobrium and denunciation seemed
sure to follow. Such a thing as privacy could scarcely
be said to exist. Having so few mental employments,
those who dwelt in these gaunt sties and pits of
the world had little beyond vagrom and errant notions
in regard to life, and spied and quarreled from sheer
ennui. They could not think sanely and consecutively.
Their interests, vivid enough at the moment, were, after
all, mere mental flutterings. They were concerned only
with what was immediately before them, the things
that at the moment they could see, hear, taste, smell,
feel. A low order of animal life, most assuredly, and
yet interesting as animal by reason of the sharp contrast afforded to the more ordered and constructive
superimposed intellectual life of other regions.

But now as to Cornelia Mullanphy, the thin, amiable
and yet eccentric, anemic and high-strung daughter
who, if such taunts as Mrs. Finnerty's were to be believed, was the true mother of the little Delia Mullanphy whom Mrs. Mullanphy claimed to be her own.
Because of fear of scandal in this region, no doubt, as
well as, possibly, previous neighborhoods in which
the family had lived, the parentage of Delia had to be
concealed. I am not sure. At any rate Cornelia was perhaps thirty-three or four, and not so ill-looking. Being
neglected and lonely, she would occasionally, as I often
had the chance to observe for myself, leave the corner

ordinarily occupied by her and her sewing machine, to visit one of the neighbors. Then would her mother's wrath pour down upon her on her return:

"Keep out of yer neighbors' rooms, you! Isn't it them that's laughin' and makin' fun of us the while? Indeed, it's Katie Tooney herself, her that ye think is yer friend, that only last week was callin' down fer all the neighbors to know that ye're not married but a man's plaything and that Delia's not my child but yours!"

"It's a lie! It's a lie!" flared Cornelia, furiously. "She never said it, and you know she didn't. You make up lies—you with yer church! Have you no peace ever! Shut yer jaw!"

"Shut me jaw, is it? Yer own mother, and me that took ye back when ye had no one, when ye couldn't get a man to look at ye! It's me that's to shut me jaw, is it?"

But in spite of Mrs. Mullanphy's raucous family and neighborly controversies, she could be as careful and silent about my place and among my spare belongings as any one could wish. Indeed at times my humble effects seemed positively to overawe her, especially such things as paintings, candelabra, silverware. There was one painting in particular, a large and well-composed nude after the manner of the neo-impressionists of 1912, which seemed actually to terrify her. Curiously enough, in her world the nude, in the form of prints, illustrations and paintings, was plainly taboo. Perhaps her church or priest condemned them. At any rate I cannot recall that ever I saw her give this particular picture one direct glance, unless it was the first one. Invariably she passed it, where it hung above a low shelf of books, with averted face and downcast eyes. The frame might need dusting, and the objects on the shelf below it, yet although everything else in the rooms was scrupulously cleaned and polished by her, these things were left untouched. She objected to the painting. It disagreed with her. Or if not that, as I have said, her church did not countenance such things.

Considering her amazing tempers and moods, however, her church, as it seemed to me, appeared to have an almost uncanny and even amazing hold on Bridget. She was a devout Catholic, blending, to my confusion, always, a kind of blind animal faith in her religion with the temperamental, material, and as I often thought, pagan notions and actions that elsewhere governed others who were wholly pagan. In short, oil and water mixed.

And because of this I once ventured to interrogate her as follows:

"Mrs. Mullanphy," I said, "I notice that you go to church very regularly. You must be a good Christian."

"And why not?" she bristled. " 'Tis from me church that I gets me stren'th. And if it wasn't for me faith, I couldn't go on at all, 'tis that hard on me life is."

"True enough," I agreed. "Life does press hard on

most of us. But I notice that in spite of your religion you have a pretty rough time of it where you are. Are all your neighbors so bad?"

"And am I to hold me tongue and that bein' said about me that's not so?" she demanded, her choler rising. "'Tis not within morshall (mortal was what she meant) patience. 'Tis not human." And she brandished the handle of an oil mop then in her hand as one might a spear, at the same time crumpling a dusting-cloth in the other hand as though it were something tangible with which to fight.

"I know, I know," I said, placatingly. "No doubt they say a lot of things about you they shouldn't. Everybody has to endure that sort of thing. But how about what the Bible says about loving your neighbor as yourself, and turning the left cheek if some one smites you on the right. Doesn't that command you to keep the peace?"

"The Bible! The Bible!" she blurted, defiantly. "Sure, and I know me Bible as well as any one, and better." (I knew she could not read.) "And I know what me church says about it, too. I can get the straight of it from me priest any day. But what about me neighbors lovin' me and lettin' me alone when I'm not doin' anything to any of them, bad end to them! Will ye tell me that? 'Tis the Bible itself says an eye for an eye and a tooth for a tooth, and I'm not forgettin' that either. 'Tis in the same book."

"Very true," I agreed. "It does say that. But this

other is what Jesus said. An eye for an eye and a tooth for a tooth is from the Old Testament. But Jesus said that he was giving a new law."

"And 'tis not any one that need be tellin' me, fer 'tis well I know it," she replied, pugnaciously. "But who'll be sayin' that I'm not within me right in defendin' me own? Isn't it meself that is forever tryin' to keep the pace wherever I am, loanin' of me salt and me coffee and me butter and the suds of me wash or the boilin's of me meat? Sure, and there would be none better than meself as a neighbor did I have them about me that had the sense. 'Tis better than this I was used to before I come to where I am to-day—the roilin's and scrapin's of New York."

"You were better born, you mean?"

"Indade and I was. The scrapin's that I have to live with this day."

"Quite so, quite so," I dishonestly soothed. "I can see that you are better than those about you, and that you do better too, really."

"Well, I'm not meanin' to say that I'm that much better than another. But sure, I'm not called to do more than me best nor more than any other. And the Lard himself never intended that any one should be more than human. He'd never have made a purgatory if he had."

"Grand," I thought. "The acme of logic. What more need I say now?" And so desisted. But hers, as you may see, was a typically confused, evasive and pagan mind coated over by a lot of religious dogma which she did not really comprehend but which she sought to blend in some confused way with the sordid routine of her daily life. Yet, as any one could also see, the blending went hard. Still, Heaven, I am sure, was a real enough place to Mrs. Mullanphy—the heaven of a patriarchal whiskered God, the Father; of the Jesus of the mediæval pictures, and the kindly Virgin of the starry crown and lilies. If she has since died and not found them seated upon a throne and surrounded by clouds as she imagined them to be, then there is one very much troubled and puzzled Irish spirit roaming about somewhere in space.

But I speak of this religious tendency not irreverently or to poke fun, as some may think—I am too sorry for blind, stumbling, seeking humanity to do anything of the sort—but because this profound religiosity of hers contrasted so oddly with her general outlook and method of procedure; with the grand frays and ebullitions of temperament that were the order of each week, excluding Sundays, which as I know were more solemnly observed—Mrs. Mullanphy attending mass and observing her other church duties with a regularity which all Catholics would no doubt look upon as commendable.

Yet in order to round out this decidedly Hogarthian atmosphere, I am, perforce, and almost against my will, compelled to introduce two other persons connected with her, and when I would so much prefer to describe her only. Those same were apparently two grand-nieces, bizarre and hoyden creatures both, who made their livings, in so far as I could gather, at housework here and there in the great city and who some time after I had known Bridget were either imported by or else had out of a clear sky descended on my heroine from Ireland. Only and except for a certain lightness or brightness which they contributed to the Mullanphy atmosphere from time to time, they really constituted a moral problem and one somewhat different, I must say, from that of Cornelia and the mysterious child. I do not mean to imply that they were not good girls in the sense that their limited intelligence could grasp good. But . . . well . . . in so far as I could gather from one and another person observing this somewhat complicated scene, they were not strictly honest. That is . . . but there, let me proceed to the painting of them and let the peculiar data take care of itself.

Molly McGragh, for instance, was tall and pale, with a round face, gray eyes and lightish brown hair, not very attractive, but with a fairly genial manner and temperament and rather addicted to gossip. By way of contrast, her sister Katie, younger by at least two years, was cheerful, good-natured, amusing, flamboyant. Where Molly was usually sober and plain in gray or white, Katie was arresting always in a suit of terra cotta or strawberry, with a red or green hat adorned with white feathers, a boa, a parasol, and I know not what else. Whenever she came, which was often, she came quite noisily. Indeed, the first day I saw her it was her voice that startled the air and myself. "Ha, he! 'Tis yerself!" (To Cornelia) "Where's the Mullanphys? Where's the grafters? Out airin' thimselves? 'Tis as well. They should get the air once in a while." Then going to the rear air-shaft and waving to a tenant occupying rooms to the rear: "Ho, ho, is it yerself, Mrs. Hanfy? And how the divil are ye?"

And then Molly: "The grafters is out, is they? The two of us swears we'll never come here again. But 'tis the nature of us brings us, I do suppose, Cornelia. We're that soft-hearted. But 'tis unnecessary to ask ye how ye are. Ye're lookin' good."

To which Cornelia, from her dusty corner and sewing machine, replied: "Sure, I'm all right. Sit down, will ye? The old man ain't workin' again. I suppose he'll be findin' somethin' pretty soon though or we won't be here long, any of us."

"Not workin', ye say?" This from Molly. "He's been idle long enough now, I'm thinkin'. And always watchin' everybody else to see whether they're workin' or not. 'Tis strange how 'tis with some folks. 'Tis a mystery to me how it is that without work he gets the drink."

But if you were to assume from this that Bridget and her husband and the McGraghs were very much at outs, you are very much mistaken. You could not judge by what you heard any more than you could believe your own eyes. The approach of one to another in this peculiar world, to say nothing of their attitude toward life, toward friendship, and what not else, was literally topsy-turvy. Thus, should the Mullanphys père and mère happen to appear in the midst of such a condemnation as I have described, you would hear "me darlin's" and "How are ye, auntie dear? Sure, 'tis weeks since we've been over, but 'tis not fer not wantin' to come. Only Chuesday of last week 'twas me that was sayin' to Katie that we must be goin' to see our Aunt Bridget and be takin' her a little of somethin' to let her know we're not ungrateful fer all she did fer us. But last week 'twas Mrs. Whitebait herself was sick on our day off. But to-day the two of us was sayin', sick or not sick we would come this day, and here we be."

"And sure, me darlin's," Mrs. Mullanphy would rejoice. "'Tis welcome ye are, too, as the flowers in May. And to dinner it is that ye'll be stayin', the two of ye. Whist, now, 'tis not much that will be in the house, I'm fearin', with Mullanphy out of work this long while, but 'twill be somethin'. The store is but a step and I can run over this minute, or Cornelia can, and will be bringin' all we need before ye can say six or ten!"

And forthwith Cornelia, who had just been declaring that her parents were slave drivers, that they "borried" from her, and that they never gave her anything for the work she did, would begin suggesting appetizing dishes that she could prepare. And the McGraghs themselves would insist on paying for what was needed, since that was obviously what Mrs. Mullanphy intended, at the same time giving each other a sly look which seemed to suggest "grafter."

But the amazing turns these same feasts and presumably gay conversations would take, and almost entirely due to the temperament of Mrs. Mullanphy, as I used to think. For first, and now that a good dinner loomed ahead of her, (the McGraghs or Cornelia having gone to the store), she would proceed to indulge in a bit of cheering banter either from the front or rear window or across the open air-shaft. Ah, how often have I listened. "And is the old man's corns better, Mrs. Hanfy? Ah, 'tis the sad infliction!" Then pausing to sniff, "And what is it ye may be cookin'? Yes, I see the smoke of it. Lamb? Eggplant, ye say? Oh, steak." Then leaning still farther out of the window and talking louder: " 'Tis not a lover of steak I am meself. What? Corned-beef hash?" Turning and facing whoever might chance to be inside, she might add, somewhat censoriously and yet not entirely so: "She don't like the smoke seen comin' from out of her room. She's closed the window on me."

But we will assume that the arrangements for dining are progressing satisfactorily enough. The young nieces have bought and paid for the proposed feast. Cornelia, given the cash, has brought it. Mullanphy, a sleepily intoxicated person and usually somewhat dour, life seeming not too much or too important to him at any time, may be stalking about in an odd, silent way, his hat on the back of his head—never off—and his coat, winter or summer, slipped back off his shoulders and hanging rather limply and crumpled between the arms. Sober and working or drunk and idle, he was, as I had observed in the course of time, never quite able to face his wife bravely and roughly and yet never wholly afraid of her—a cross between a man who has never been wholly subdued and one who is still afraid to say too much.

Suddenly, in the midst of this, and after setting out to do all the cooking, and apparently not wishing to be interfered with in that quarter, Mrs. Mullanphy would bethink herself of the fact that whosoever might have paid for the dinner, it was she and none other who was cooking it, the McGraghs and others lolling about. Presto! "Mullanphy! Mullanphy! Will ye be standin' there and lettin' the steak burn up on me? And me with a dozen other things on me hands at once, and the coffee not boiled yet!"

Yet despite this and for all his awe of and therefore respect for his somewhat difficult and threatening wife, Mullanphy would know well enough that this shot was not for him. Rather, and as seemingly direct as it was, he would look blankly back from one of the front windows where he was standing, but without a word. On the other hand, Katie and Molly, and even Cornelia, for whom the remark was really intended, would run from whatever they were doing and come to the rescue, only decidedly resentful and ready to fight.

"Sure, Aunt Bridget," Katie might exclaim in an injured tone, "if ye want us to help you in the first place, why didn't ye say so? Certainly ye needn't make it look as though we didn't want to help." Then Mrs. Mullanphy, throwing up both hands and shaking her head, would wail: "If I'm not the unfortunate woman! If I'm not the persecuted one with ye, Katie McGragh! To think and I cannot talk but ye must be mistakin' the meaning of me. 'Tis Mullanphy himself who well knows 'tis his place to give me help, and dinner for six on the fire. If I do lose me temper, 'tis not with ye, or Cornelia either, but with him that should be helpin' me and never does."

And yet Mullanphy would stand there without a word. And Katie and Molly and Cornelia merely exchanging looks. And then presently, of course, there would be peace for the time being and more gassing about the neighbors until, and possibly because of, the loud talk and the air carrying the sounds across the halls and through the windows, there would be renewed argument between one neighbor and another and Mrs. Mullanphy and the nieces and Mullanphy or all, separately or collectively by turns. The "roilin's and scrapin's," as it were.

But to return to these nieces. One of the phases of Mrs. Mullanphy's dealings with them which puzzled me not a little, and concerning which as yet I have said nothing, was her somewhat lax and certainly far from religious or even moral attitude toward their rather moral-less point of view in regard to what can only be described as the property of others. And that in the face of her continued religious and conventional criticism of others. For her nieces, as well as her daughter, as I gradually came to know, were inclined to purloin things from their various employers (quite numerous during the course of several years)—food, clothing, et cetera —and presently bring the same to Mrs. Mullanphy, who, as she was wont to declare, got her "stren'th" from her church. Only she took these same spoils, as I am very truly able to state, with some weak, if moral, reflection to the effect that extreme necessity tends to excuse deeds of this kind, however little it may repeal moral law. But how do I know all this? Well, for one thing, at one time there was one who lived on the floor above the Mullanphys and with whom they as well as myself were friendly, and who told me many amusing tales of strange goings-on in this respect. On the other hand, there were my own personal observations, based on a desire to know, as well as overheard scraps and long conversations with one or another of these same characters in these same halls or rooms.

But regardless of this, some of the facts in regard to these dishonestly-come-by gains relate to a certain afternoon in October, at which time the two nieces arrived from where they had been working—deserted because of unsatisfactory conditions—bearing between them half of a ham, a quarter of a side of bacon, two dozen eggs, a can of coffee, a package of tea, a table-cloth, and a few more such items, all of which and themselves included were received with open arms by Mrs. Mullanphy—who subsequently fell out with them because they stayed too long with her before getting another place. And yet the friendship and perhaps the generous purloining continued unbroken. Again there was Cornelia, who, I was once told, returned from her place of employment one afternoon, when Mr. and Mrs. Mullanphy and one of the nieces were present, fairly laden with spoils. One of her trophies—which she brought forth from under the voluminous cape she wore—was a yellow plush album containing portraits of people in no way related to her.

" 'Tis the color of it that I like most," was her reported comment.

"And ye divil!" her mother's only reply, the while she admired the binding.

"When I only get a dollar and me meals for seven or eight hours' slavin', 'tis small blame to me to help meself," the intrepid robber is alleged to have announced.

On the other hand, Mrs. Mullanphy was not without a form of charity for others, as the following incident will show.

On the ground floor of her place lived the Kiltys—

husband, wife, and fragile daughter of eleven or twelve.
A grown-up son had disappeared. At one time,
not so long after the above, they were about
to be dispossessed for non-payment of rent.
Michael Kilty, the father, was in many respects even
worse than Mullanphy. He was no good at all. A
bricklayer by trade, for one reason or another—drink,
indifference, laziness—he had degenerated to the point
where he was almost always out of work, and out of
the masons' union also, an organization which had
apparently dismissed him for his various sins. In the
face of this he did not hesitate to "scab," a thing
which infuriated the union men. Even when he did
work, though, he would often disappear and leave
his wife for six or eight weeks at a time. At other
times, having loafed a long time and not having
a cent on him, he would come home in rags, or
sick, or at least pretending to be, and would hang
around promising to do better when he got well and
would then send his wife out to do washing until she
too would fall ill. Yet for some reason she would endure all this, and more—ill-treatment of a physical
nature, even so much as a beating from time to time.

On one occasion this model father, having been
away for a long time and his wife in his absence
having fallen ill and because of this having been
unable to work, the Kilty furniture was about
to be set out on the street. But Mrs. Mullanphy, having
had few, if any, fights with Mrs. Kilty, whom she con-

sidered a deserving and much put-upon woman, was, at the last moment, moved to sympathy. What, the poor sick things to be set out on the sidewalk? Sure, all landlords were bloodsuckers and divils! Was not hers a true Irish heart, and would a true Irish heart go back on any other true Irish heart in its hour of distress? Scarcely. So, in the afternoon of the day the notice had been served on the Kiltys, and after the news had been spread and discussed throughout the building and no one had come to the rescue, she made her way down to their floor.

"Sure," she announced on her arrival, and referring to landlords and real estate dealers in general, " 'tis the divil's own brood they are, fattenin' on the bodies of the pore! 'Tis none of them that has the heart of a snake, or the dacency either, to see how it is with the pore. But what is it the paper says, anyhow—the notice? One of ye read it to me, 'tis me eyes that are bad." (As I said before, she could not read.)

" 'Pay to-morrow at noon or be required to vacate said premises,' " read Norah Kilty. " 'This letter is in legal form and no other notice will be necessary.' "

" 'Tis not worth the paper 'tis written on," exclaimed Mrs. Mullanphy, who because of many previous instances in which she herself, you may be sure, had been the subject of such a notice, had acquired at least the rudiments of proper legal procedure in all such cases. "Sure, the old divil's written ye this to save expenses. It costs from two-fifty to eight dollars for the regular notice, accordin' to the fees of the marshal and the marshal's men. And the landlord has to put everything out on the street in perfect order or ye can collect on him. Yes indeed, so 'tis. And what's more, Mrs. Kilty, 'tis often a good plan in these cases to loosen up the back of a mirror or some such thing so 'twill fall out and break, fer nothin' is supposed to be broke. Nothin'! And 'tis such things as might be helpin' ye to get a start, ye understand? The court would be holdin', maybe, that what with damage and all that, a little somethin' might be due ye, ye see? 'Tis not that I speak of this by any experience of me own, y'understand, but 'tis not the first case of dispossess I see, either."

"Oh, wurra, wurra! Oh me, oh me!" wailed Mrs. Kilty. " 'Tis not the wit I have to do it. 'Tis not the wit nor the strenth either. And me old man out of work this three months now. And me son Tim away and down with pneumony in Philadelphy. And meself that upset with trouble and not knowin' how to do next. If only me husband was the sober man he might be, and with a better heart for the jobs he do get . . . !"

"But what becomes of the furniture once it do be set out, Mrs. Mullanphy, if ye know?" This from Mrs. Hanfy, another inquisitive and sympathetic neighbor who had edged in and was eager to know the ins and out of dispossess proceedings generally.

"Sure, and I know very little of these cases except as I have seen 'em here and there in me time," replied

Mrs. Mullanphy, loftily and aloofly. "We was never dispossessed ourselves, but 'tis me recollection that unless the furniture be took away again be the tenant, the Bureau of Encumbrances moves it to the City Yard. 'Tis the laa, I believe. Only, be what I hear—'tis all hearsay, y'understand—ye must go down and see about it within twenty-four hours else the Bureau of Encumbrances can do whatever they please with it. But whisht ye!" she added, as Mrs. Kilty burst into a fresh fit of weeping. " 'Tis not so bad as ye're after thinkin'. 'Tis the judge of the district that can do somethin' fer ye, too. 'Tis to him ye must go with the notice. This be the Eight District—Charlless Street—if I'm not mistaken, and 'tis to the judge of the court there ye must go. Me darter Cornelia will be after goin' with ye if ye like. But, sure, any policeman can be tellin' ye where to go. Maybe ye can get a stay from the judge. Sometimes if ye be after tellin' him a sad story, 'tis easy to take a week's time at least. And between that and the work ye may get and the expenses to the landlord ye may bring on him by way of damage to yer furniture, ye can maybe make out. 'Tis me that has seen it done before." Yet in the face of this Mrs. Kilty continued to cry, whereupon Mrs. Mullanphy continued: "And sure, and ye're not the first whose furniture was set out on the street fer want of a bit of rent. In these days, and with the wolves that is ownin' property, 'tis small wonder."

"'Tis hard, 'tis hard," interpolated Mrs. Hanby at this point.

"Sure an' 'tis," continued Mrs. Mullanphy. "But listen, 'tis easy to tell a sad story. Sure, any one can do it. 'Twould be better, of course, if ye had a child or two—a baby in arms is the best—but since ye have a husband and son sick and out of work, 'tis as well. So don't be taken on so. Besides, there be lots of children in the house. Let ye but ask fer the loan of two. Ye pay yer rent to the agent, don't ye, the same as the rest of us? Well then, they'll not be after knowin' whether the children are yer own or not. Once ye're before the judge, ye can say ye have the little ones to look after and no place to go this night. 'Tis no judge in New York will turn ye out, and ye with children to look after. 'Tis meself would be lettin' ye have the rent an' I had it. But Delia ye may take fer me if ye will. For I'll not be seein' ye turned out on the streets at that. If the judge won't be givin' ye more time, ye can come with me for a day or two. Room fer yer things I have not, but as for you and Norah, yes. No doubt your husband will be lookin' fer another place the while, and yerself too, and findin' somethin'."

But as it turned out, Mrs. Kilty being sick and not having the courage to go before the judge with a borrowed child as her own, the furniture was set out on the sidewalk and removed by the Bureau of Encumbrances. And Mrs. Kilty and her daughter having been escorted to the Mullanphy apartment, it was not twenty-four hours before Kilty returned, and finding his wife thus comfortably housed and no rent to pay, fixed himself, by a process of blather and a hard luck story and promises, upon the Mullanphys also. But after three or four days of this, and no sign on the part of Kilty that he was developing any intention to work, (although Mrs. Kilty was out seeking something to do), Mrs. Mullanphy's "true Irish" rose. Only, instead of taking the situation directly in hand and ordering them out, her curiously involute and roundabout nature dictated an entirely different course. Better to hint, and hint broadly, as in the case of her nieces, but more for the benefit of Kilty than for his wife and daughter. And with her husband, whether by pre-arrangement or not I could never guess, serving as a foil or false target. Thus all would be gathered in the combination dining room and kitchen. Kilty would be lounging near the mantel, behind the stove, where it was warmest. Mrs. Mullanphy, her aproned sides slanting wide, would be seated at the table. Mrs. Kilty and her daughter, mayhap, would be engaged in cleaning up after dinner, Mrs. Mullanphy having done the work of preparing it.

Sewing or mending, but contemplating with dissatisfied eyes the imperturbable Kilty, who would be calmly smoking a pipe and meditating, hands on stomach, she would finally reach the point where the sight of him would be too much for her, and would begin, presumably addressing her husband:

"Oh, but it's you that knows how to live without hurtin' yer health, it is. The idler that ye are, Mullanphy the loafer." Whereupon Mullanphy, knowing full well that this was not for him but Kilty, would shift perhaps a trifle uneasily and yet not wholly uncomfortably, and perhaps after a time, seeing his wife's eyes fixed steadily upon him, would turn to Kilty, who without a trace of embarrassment, might continue to rest as before, and inquire: "Ye've found nothin' in yer line to-day again, I suppose, Kilty?"

"Not to-day, no," would the imperturbable Kilty reply. "There's plenty of work for union men, of course, if only me card was good, but not for the likes of me in the shape I'm in now. I did go into four places, though. There's a job over at the car company, I hear. None but non-union men there. I'm goin' over there in the mornin'. If it's not more than four hundred brick a day, I can manage in me present state, I think."

And at this Mullanphy, his duty done, might resume his former contemplative position. But not so his wife, who was not to be put off so easily.

"Ah, four hundred brick; 'tis a lot for one man to lay, I suppose. But 'tis a gentleman's life *you* lead, Mullanphy, just the same, and without even that much work, makin' yerself comfortable where it's warm and no meals to pay for. 'Tis you I mean, Mullanphy; always idle, always 'tis somethin' that stops ye from findin' somethin'. Sure, and 'tis a wonder to me that any women find anythin' to do these days, 'tis so hard men be findin' it to get anything at all."

But the shrewd Kilty was by no means so easily to be routed. On the contrary, slyer and more dissolute than Mullanphy, and as cunning and much more callous than even Mrs. Mullanphy (who was cunning enough), and with the effrontery of the devil himself, he would "stick" or "sit tight," as we say the while such broadsides as the above were leveled at him. But not so either his wife or daughter, who daily sought work. Yet in this instance the last straw was finally laid by himself when some three or four days later—and after this much sponging—he finally arrived on the scene one evening, drunk and with a drunken companion, cut and bleeding from having been thrown out of a saloon. It was Mrs. Mullanphy who, peeling potatoes at the time, saw him first; and then Mullanphy, breaking the slats of a green-grocer's box on the window sill with a flat iron. Mrs. Kilty and her daughter were sitting about rather helplessly. Cornelia was working out and had not returned as yet. Little Delia was playing in the street below.

Mrs. Mullanphy's first impulse as the door opened and the two bums stood revealed, one holding the other up, was to shout: "Mullanphy, by the Blessed Mother of God!" The stranger's cheek and forehead were badly cut and smeared with blood and Kilty was saying most helpfully: "Wait'll I tie a rag around yer head. That'll fix it. Wait'll ye wash the blood off, then ye'll be all right when yer head's tied up."

But Mrs. Mullanphy did not think so. "Jesus, Mary and all the Blessed Saints!" she exclaimed. "I could never stand the sight o' blood. I'm faint, Mullanphy. Will no one be puttin' the likes of that out o' here? Will ye be lettin' the likes o' that in here?"

Whereupon Mullanphy drew dubiously if by no means threateningly nearer.

But Kilty, drunk, was by no means to be dismayed at this reception. On the contrary, he was all cheer and hope. "Will ye let me explain, Mrs. Mullanphy?" he pleaded, genially, the while he sustained his companion as best he might. "He's only been cut, see? Some bums up at the job where we was workin' jumped on him. We was workin' on a job, see, and some bums . . ."

"Yes, 'tis well I know who the bums was! And as for the job, I know that, too. Job, indeed! Mullanphy, will ye be after lettin' the two of them come in here? Ain't it enough that they be eatin' us out of house and home but must be searchin' the streets fer bums, as if there wasn't a houseful here now? And me workin' and slavin', and yerself and Cornelia, too, fer the likes o' them. Have ye no spunk at all? Must I be slavin' here and not enough to eat in the house as 'tis?"

At this the shameless and undaunted Kilty had the drunken effrontery to come forward and exclaim: " 'Tisn't dinner he's after, Mrs. Mullanphy. 'Tisn't that.

He's had his dinner, see? We both have. 'Tis his face; 'tis his face he wants to wash up. I'm only bringin' him in to wash his face, see?"

"And to stay the night, yes, like yerself. And to breakfast in the mornin'. And to supper the morrow night again. And after that for weeks and months like yerself and yer family that ye won't support. 'Tis more than morshall patience can bear. And scarce room to move and breathe as 'tis, Mullanphy."

And Mullanphy, now coming forward, added: "Say, now, this *is* too much, Kilty. Man, ye can't expect to bring yerself and him in the fix he's in here. 'Tis to the hospital he should go."

"Yes, after he's fixed his face. Yes, sure, after he's fixed his head."

"No, not after he fixes his head, but right now!" This from the now thoroughly aroused Mrs. Mullanphy. "And yerself and yer wife and yer darter. To be sure, I pities them more than I do you, but 'tis the lot of ye must go. Is Mullanphy and meself to be workin' to feed a regiment? Is there no end to the lot o' ye, and will ye be searchin' the streets fer more? Then out of me sight with the lot of ye! And go laughin' to yerself fer the fool you've made of Bridget Mullanphy!"

By this time Mrs. Kilty and Norah, seeing the trouble that had been brought upon them by this worthless head of their family, were meekly packing up their belongings, making bundles of little things and rolling them up. Incidentally putting on extra skirts, one above the other, and pointing out silently to each other the things they had forgotten.

"Be sure, Mrs. Mullanphy," coaxed the artful Kilty, "ye don't want to get so excited. You're takin' the wrong meanin' out o' this."

"Wrong meanin', is it? And me provisions laid away for the winter gone this long time, and no money to pay the rent that's due this Chuesday next? Daylight robbers! Midnight robbers! That's what ye are! Not yer wife, but you!"

"Ah, well," conceded Kilty, realizing at last the futility of coaxing, "if ye don't want us to stay here, that's all right. We can go some place else. Sure, we can. Come on, Mike, I can take ye to a hospital." And down the steps they lurched.

"And 'tis good riddance to the both of ye!" shouted Mrs. Mullanphy after them. "But who's to give me back me butter, of which ye ate five pounds, and me fish and me steak and me flour? Where's the bottle of relish that lasted but the one meal? That the divil might have choked ye with it! Robbers! Robbers!"

"We're very sorry, Mrs. Mullanphy," pleaded the humble Norah Kilty, frightened out of her wits at this storm. "We're goin' now. 'Tis that sorry we are to have been the cause of so much trouble." And Mrs. Kilty added: "Yes, we are that. We're goin' right now. 'Tis more than sorry I am fer all the trouble I've brought on ye, and 'twasn't fer him I wouldn't have stayed the time I did, but 'twas he that made me."

"And well I know it, the robber! But 'tis not fer yerself that I'm talkin', but fer him, the robber! 'Tis the likes of him and his bums that has brought ye where ye are this day, Mrs. Kilty. But the good Lord himself wouldn't be after feedin' him and his drunken friends and the lot of ye into the bargain. But 'tis to-night ye'll be stayin', or to-morrow maybe, the two of ye, now that he's gone." Her tone softened.

But no, the Kiltys would not, and sensibly enough under the circumstances. Instead they went crying down the stairs after Kilty had disappeared with his friend and were neither seen nor heard of more, in so far as I know.

About this time, the agent of the building in which I rented a floor chanced to ask me whether I knew any one who would, for the gift of one or two rooms in the basement, rent free, perform the duties of a janitress. I immediately suggested Mrs. Mullanphy. For despite all of her rowing with her neighbors and their charges in regard to her cleanliness or lack of cleanliness, she was really comparatively clean. More, having heard her asseverate so often how much better she would do if surrounded by those who would let her alone, I suggested to this agent that if he would instruct her sharply as to possible visitors and the heinousness of loud talking, let alone shouting or quarreling—for which there was small opportunity in this very different vicinity—I thought all would be well. And should she fail to behave herself, of course she was to be compelled to vacate at once.

And following this advice of mine, and with a clear understanding of what was desired, as I assumed, came Mrs. Mullanphy and Mullanphy also, his coat below his shoulders, as always, and Cornelia and little Delia, and in due time the two nieces, Molly and Katie Mc-Gragh—with such rags of furniture as I will not trouble to describe. Only finding me master of the parlor floor and others like myself living above, the entire family, for a short time at least, was very quiet, Mrs. Mullanphy, for one, devoting herself to washing and cleaning for all, the others working, and no quarrels that I could hear between them. Only—and just the same—and quarreling or no quarreling—tragedy, as I might have expected, since with or because of the combination of personal ties about them, neither Mrs. Mullanphy nor her daughter were suitable for the work in hand. Their social standards were a little too decayed. Also, and via this same tragedy, a clear white light on the mystery of Cornelia and little Delia.

For one hot summer afternoon, after all had been in this new place some four or five months, there arrived outside Mrs. Mullanphy's basement door a small, pinched, intense and decidedly distrait-looking Irish woman, who after knocking and ringing with great violence at the Mullanphy door and the two basement windows—which seemed for the occasion to have been closed and shuttered against her—took a position before one of them (and this same just below one of mine which was directly above) and began calling. But what? For a long time I did not know what this droning voice was, and only by opening one of my windows did I at last gather the import of it.

"Come out, now! Come out, ye ———! Come out, ye ———! Come out, and I'll teach ye to let me husband alone! Ye ———, you! Ye ———, you! Come on out now! Come on out!"

And so on and on and over and over, like a droning fly with the little woman rattling at the shutters or the iron basement gate, betimes, but no faintest noise or sign from within. Yet that some of the Mullanphy family were below I well knew, for only a little time before there had been voices which had been audible enough through a rear area-way. None the less, silence. And with the little woman trying, as I could see, to peer through the blinds.

After a considerable time, however, during which a street crowd began to gather—first a few small children, then men and women—and the noise of this same becoming loud with inquiry or wonder—that same basement hall door under the outside stoop opened and Cornelia Mullanphy stepped forth. A strange girl, or woman, that Cornelia, grotesque and a little sad, as I always thought, with her thin, angular body, high cheek bones, red hair, and her of course confused and befuddled because inadequate mind. And always, as I had long noted, in staccato colors, a green or red or

yellow shirtwaist, coupled with a brown or dark green
skirt. And this very day the same—bizarre, flamboyant. Also her manner, as I had often noted, was a
little flighty. And this day the same—a girl or woman
who seemed weakly and so helplessly drawn to men,
but one who had, none the less, never proved very
attractive to any, or at least few, and, in consequence, I
assume, spiritually distrait. And behind her on this
occasion her mother, unusually nervous and pale, as
I thought (the neighborhood overawing her somewhat,
I presume), and saying as she came: "Have no words
with her, I say! Have no words with her, fer the love
o' God! 'Tis nonsense to have words with her, I say!"

But for all of that, the intense and dour Cornelia
paying no attention, her face very white, her
eyes narrowed. Instead exclaiming—and that most defiantly for her: "Who're ye callin' those names to, say?
Who?" And glaring. As a matter of fact, she was quite
dramatic, far more picturesque and intense than ever
she had seemed before.

" 'Tis well ye know who I'm talkin' to, ye ———,
you!" exclaimed the little woman from a higher level,
to which at the sound of the basement door opening
she had retreated. " 'Tis yerself that I'm callin', ye
———! 'Tis you that'll not be lettin' me man
alone, but must be runnin' after him, and him
the father of two children, and you not able
to get a man of yer own! 'Tis well I know of
ye from Barry Street, ye ———! And with a child of

yer own that has no father but must be owned by yer mother for ye!"

"Say that again and I'll slap yer face fer ye!" declared the infuriated Cornelia, stepping close.

" 'Tis me that says it, and 'tis you that knows it's true!" insisted the stranger. " 'Tis Cornelia Dempsey ye are that lived in Barry Street, and not Mullanphy, and 'tis me man that ye're tryin' to take from me this day, since ye can't get one of yer own, ye ——— you!"

At this, smack came the hand of the intense, white Cornelia square across the mouth and cheek of the older woman, and then smack again from the other side. "I'll show ye whether ye'll rattle me windows and say what ain't so!"

At first the intruder appeared to be completely stunned by this—beaten, no less, for she fell back, white and weak—the crowd, of course of whom I made one, gazing in amaze. Then: "Aha!" hissed the little woman, laying at the same time a thin, worn hand across her mouth and cheek. "Aha!" And then: "But wait! You'll strike me, will ye? And after tryin' to steal me husband from me! But wait! 'Tis not the last of me or you! I'll be back!" And off she started up the hot, sunlit street, at first walking very fast and then as her shame and rage grew, breaking into an odd, awkward lope until as she approached the nearest corner she turned, and disappeared. But not for long, as she said. She was soon back. Only in the meantime, the cautious Bridget, now very much excited, had seized her irate daughter by the shoulders and pulled her down into and through the basement door and closed it.

But as I say, in a few minutes (the doors and windows below stairs still tightly closed and the place silent) the little woman returned. But this time with nothing less than an ax in her hand—a large, hard, glistening ax. And behind her, trailing, two children, her own as I could tell, but following without her consent. For, as I pictured it all to myself, she must have rushed into her home and out again, her children amazedly seeing her seize the ax and then following after her. But as I could now see, her mood was really murderous—no thought of fear or compromise this time. And at once she began as before, only in much louder tone, the while she banged at the shutters with the ax. "Come out, now . . ." etc., etc.

Indeed so white was she and panting, that as she struck the first blow I seized my telephone and called for the police, explaining, as soon as I had the neighborhood station house, that the situation was desperate. Also that a large crowd was gathering. Whereupon an officer was promised at once. Then I returned to the window and listened to such an outburst as I had scarcely ever heard before—never in that neighborhood—the wronged Irish wife now shouting her ills at the top of her voice, and banging the shutters with such violence as finally to break one through. The scandal, the disgrace, I thought. And now, no doubt, murder into the bargain. And I had brought them here. Ye Gods—my own studio in danger of being forfeited. I was in real distress, as I can tell you.

By this time, however, the policeman for whom I had first called had arrived, also teamsters from a livery stable over the way, and storekeepers, saloonkeepers —the riffraff as well as the well-dressed pedestrians, and children from all the neighboring houses—a huge crowd which blocked traffic and stared in amazement at this odd figure with her ax and two children. Yet not a sound from the rooms below; not a whisper. And the police now demanding in sharp, aggressive tones: "And what's the trouble here now? Why will ye be here in broad daylight destroyin' property? Is it murder ye want to do? Let me have the ax now." And, much to my personal relief, seizing and securing the ax even as he spoke.

But the little woman still continuing to shout. And the two children crying. And the crowd now buzzing, murmuring, even laughing or cat-calling—some yoohooing and even whistling—the result of a fiasco, I assume. None the less, as I saw it, a most scandalous scene, and one that I by my recommendation to my landlord had brought about. And what would he say now when he heard of this? What excuse could I offer? For he was a none too liberal, in fact highly conventional, landlord, who seemed always to think that I too was conventional. Ah, my honorable life! My previous good name! I feared the worst for myself as well as the family below, but wondered still more about the attitude of Mrs. Mullanphy. Why the quiet? Why no defiance, no martial display of dust-pan and broom, or mop and washrag? A most amazing stillness this—one such as I would not have deemed possible in her case, and especially under such circumstances. And yet so it was.

In due course, though, the police had succeeded not only in disarming and removing the violent visitor—taking her away and advising her, I suppose, to see a lawyer and file an action—but in dispersing the crowd also. None the less, and for hours after that, and even several days, not the lifting of a curtain or the opening of a door, not even after evening fell. Yet up the rear area-way, between six and seven the next evening, the most subdued of voices—where I could scarcely detect—in whispered conversation. And sometime after midnight, more talk. And then Mullanphy and Mrs. Mullanphy and Cornelia going out. But where? And then two days after—and due, no doubt, to a suggestion on the part of the landlord—a small, dusty moving van, removing their few and humble belongings. And then silence. They were gone. Moved. But with no word to me or any one. And after that I never saw either Cornelia or Delia or the two nieces again.

But a curious thing. Some three or four years later I began to use for cleaning purposes a sometimes drunken, and always impoverished and down at heels,

yet rather intelligent and interesting Village character—Johnny Morton by name—who did odd jobs such
as scrubbing, cleaning, washing windows, and the like
for various Greenwich Villagers. Some seemed to find
him amusing as well as useful and so were pleased
to have him around, although quite frequently he was
either too drunk or weak from dissipation to fulfill his
stipulated agreements at fifty cents an hour and so
earn his daily bread. Worse, he was, among other
things, as I subsequently learned, an ex-convict and a
dope addict, one who rather more than less bore the
marks of both. His was a wasted and worthless look at
times, so querulous, blue-nosed, nervous, and generally
rickety as to be pitiable. But when sober he was genial
and obliging, and useful enough, courteous as well as
humorous. For a long time when he was about my
place I paid not the least attention to him. He did my
work and did it fairly well, and I paid him and let
him go. But then one day, being in an unusually
genial and communicative mood, he announced: "I
used to live around here, you know." He was industriously polishing a brass coal-box in the middle of
my studio floor at the time.

"Yes?"

"Yep, sure. I was born over here on Barrow Street."
A slight sniff. He was always sniffing as though afflicted
with a perpetual cold, or scratching as though afflicted
with fleas, or wiping his nose with his coat sleeve.

"Barrow Street can at least lay claim to something then," I commented.

"Yep, sure. My old man used to be head harness man in that old stable at Tenth and Waverly."

"Really? Well, just what do you mean—harness man?"

"He kept all the harness in order, you know, shined and oiled all the harnesses of the horses, forty-fifty sets a day. I used to help him when I was a kid. Many's the kick I'd get fer not keepin' 'em shined right."

"Indeed! Pleasant youthful memories," I commented.

"Yep, sure. That's right. (Sniff.) The old man was pretty quick that way. Bad tempered. He used to drink and he was all the worse when he was drunk. He's not so bad now, though, I hear. He's gettin' older."

"Natural enough," I commented. "Age will do that. You see him occasionally then, I take it."

"Yep."

"But you don't live at home?"

"Who, me? Oh, no!" This last with a swipe of coat sleeve across his nose. "They wouldn't have me. I ain't lived at home for years now, ever since I ran away. The old man wouldn't have me now, nor the old woman either, I guess. I wouldn't ask 'em to. But I see 'em around just the same. They got sore about something I did. But I could get along with my mother if it wasn't for the old man. She ain't so bad."

(Fairly complimentary to one's mother, I thought, all

things considered.) "And what is your real name, Johnny?" I ventured. "I never did think to ask you before."

"Who, me? Oh, well, I go by the name of Morton now, since the family don't like to have me around any more, but my real name is Dempsey. My mother and father changed their name, too, to Mullanphy. But Dempsey is the real name. I got 'em into some trouble, see, and they changed the name."

Aha, I said to myself! Then a little after: "Jabez Mullanphy, by any chance? I used to know a man around here by that name."

"Why, sure, he's me father. Yuh know him? He used to be a teamster after he left the livery stable." He seemed to be a little startled himself.

"Yes, I think I know him, and your mother, too. They lived here in Bank Street once, didn't they, about five or six years ago?"

"Yep, sure. Did my mother ever do any work for you?"

"Well, not directly. I lived in a house where she did some work though."

"Well, I guess that's her. Big woman with gray hair?"

"Yes."

"My mother wouldn't be so bad," he volunteered, rather indifferently now that the interest of this discovery had paled, "if she didn't have such an awful temper. Gee, but she's got a rough temper! But the old man made her that way, I guess. He never would do what he ought to do, nor me, either—work or anything."

At this point, and without any particular emotion that I could see, he launched into a long dissertation on family ties, family duties, and the like. I gathered that, besides the daughter Cornelia, there was this same Johnny, but no other child. Hence little Delia must be Cornelia's, and so the mystery was at last solved. But no word from Johnny as to the child. He did not say and I would not ask. After that he drifted out of my life and I never saw him again.

But about three years after this conversation I chanced to change cars one noon hour at Times Square. The crowds! The rush! You know. Nearing the stairs leading down to the Seventh Avenue platform I heard a voice, a familiar one, as it seemed to me, bewailing and anxious.

"Oh-h-h-h, where is he? Where's me man? Mullanphy, in God's name, where are ye? Where's he gone to? In God's name, Mullanphy! I've lost him! My God! Ow-w-w, what'll I do now? And not a nickel on me! Ow! And where's he gone? Me old man! I'm lost! Oh-h-h!"

And turning, sure enough, there stood Mrs. Mullanphy in the flesh. A little stouter, a little grayer even— not much—a little dustier, maybe, but lurching and pitching like a ship in a heavy sea, ascending the steps inside the subway while I was descending them. And behind her, at a distance but following because he heard her shrieks and wondered what it was all about, Mullanphy himself. The same blank and yet equivocal expression on his face, his hat for once not on the back of his head, a rag of a gray overcoat over his shoulders. And trying to catch up with his bulky wife, who was lurching directly away from him and who had evidently lost track of him in the crush. Finally, catching up with her, he yelled: "Where're ye goin', ye old fool? Can't ye see I'm right here? Didn't ye just folly me down these steps a minute ago?"

"And why the divil didn't ye stay near me?" came the old, quick, defiant and irritated reply. "And what'll ye be galootherin' here and there fer and me not able to keep up with ye? And without a cent in me pocket and me not knowin' where 'tis ye're goin' anyhow! Give me me fare! Give me me fare, and thin ye can go where ye like and I'll go where I like."

A large percentage of the crowd, hurrying as it was, paused to chortle and guffaw. Fine, I thought! The old Mullanphy spirit! Not dead yet. And despite so many ills. Hurrah! Her goodly soul has not been utterly crushed, thanks be! She does live. And she can fight, hale and forceful as ever.

Yet with the nervous fear of being recognized and seized upon as an old friend in the midst of this exciting confab, I dashed into an inrushing express which was just stopping, and which plainly they were not taking, and was whisked away. But not without a backward and even sentimental look. For had there not been Barrow Street? The sisters McGragh, the dour-minded Cornelia, that awful scene in Tenth Street? Great! Life vigorous and wilful if degraded, pitiful and strange. Yet why, as I consoled myself, renew our old and always amicable relations? Was she not doing well enough, apparently? And I also. I thought so. Comparatively so, at any rate. But oh, that hearty, defiant Irish-ness, so to say. The upstanding vigor amidst all ills.

And because of these speculative musings in regard to this same Bridget Mullanphy, her troubles and her temper, I was carried two stations past my getting-off place. And proceeded to grumble at her for that.

THE END